DELTICS

R.M. Tufnell

ISBN 0 85429 430 9

A FOULIS Railway Book

First published 1985

Published by:
Haynes Publishing Group
Sparkford,
Yeovil,
Somerset BA22 7JJ

Haynes Publications Inc.
861 Lawrence Drive,
Newbury Park,
California 91320, USA

Produced by:
Winchmore Publishing Services Limited,
40 Triton Square,
London NW1 3HG

Printed in England

Titles in the *Super Profile* series:

BSA Bantam (F333)
MV Agusta America (F334)
Norton Commando (F335)
Honda CB750 sohc (F351)
Sunbeam S7 & S8 (F363)
BMW R69 & R69S (F387)

Austin-Healey 'Frogeye' Sprite (F34
Ferrari 250GTO (F308)
Fiat X1/9 (F341)
Ford GT40 (F332)
Jaguar E-Type (F370)
Jaguar D-Type & XKSS (F371)
Jaguar Mk 2 Saloons (F307)
Lotus Elan (F330)
MGB (F305)
MG Midget & Austin-Healey Sprite (except 'Frogeye') (F344)
Morris Minor & 1000 (ohv) (F331)
Porsche 911 Carrera (F311)
Triumph Stag (F342)

Avro Vulcan (F436)
B29 Superfortress (F339)
Boeing 707 (F356)
de Havilland Mosquito (F422)
Harrier (F357)
Mikoyan-Gurevich MiG 21 (F439)
P51 Mustang (F423)
Phantom II (F376)
Sea King (F377)
SEPECAT Jaguar (F438)
Super Etendard (F378)
Tiger Moth (F421)
Bell UH-1 Iroquois (F437)

Deltics (F430)
Great Western Kings (F426)
Green Arrow (F427)
Gresley Pacifics (F429)
InterCity 125 (F428)
Royal Scot (F431)

Further titles in this series will be published at regular intervals. For information on new titles please contact your bookseller or write to the publisher.

Library of Congress Catalog
Card Number
Deltics 84-48790

Deltics super profile — (Super profile)
1. Diesel Locomotives — Great Britain
1. Tufnell, R.M. 11. Series
625. 2'662'0941 TJ619
ISBN 0-85429-430-9

Contents

The Deltic Diesel Engine

The Napier 'Deltic' diesel engine was quite unique among diesel engines being triangular in shape and having three crankshafts. It was also of the two-stroke opposed-piston variety having inlet and exhaust ports with the admission and exhaust controlled by separate pistons. The basis of the design went back to 1929 when the German Aero engine firm of Junkers had produced a two-stroke opposed-piston diesel engine for aircraft applications. In 1926 the Scottish firm of Wm. Beardmore & Son Ltd had been commissioned to build some diesel engines for the R.101 airship, but the power/weight ratio of those were not adequate for use in an aeroplane. At that time the two-stroke engine could produce more power for its weight than a four-stroke engine and that led to the development of the Junkers JUMO 205 engine. This was a six-cylinder model opposed-piston engine with two crankshafts which produced 600 hp and was used in both civil and in military aircraft.

In 1930 the firm of D. Napier & Son Ltd of Acton had negotiated the rights to build the JUMO engine, but apart from a couple of engines and some test flights nothing came of this till after World War II. Napier's had originated in Lambeth in 1808 and had quickly got into the internal combustion engine market, producing both petrol engines and automobiles. They had been one of the first firms to use the new motor track at Brooklands and in 1907 achieved a record of 1,581 miles (2,544 km) in 24 hours. The Napier LION aero engine, first produced in 1918, established world speed records on land, on water and in the air, so by 1947 they were well suited to undertake a development contract to produce a lightweight high-powered marine diesel engine.

At that time the highest rated engine of that type was the Daimler-Benz 20-cylinder VEE engine which developed 2,000 hp at 1,500 rpm and had been the reason why the German 'E' boats had been superior in speed during World War II. In 1942 Napier had built the first of their SABRE aero engines with an output of 2,000 hp and at that time the highest output of any engine for that application. That engine was built on the 'H' formation with two crankshafts geared together. Junkers had designed a variation of their JUMO 205 engine with four crankshafts and four banks of cylinders in a square formation with an intended output of 2,400 hp, but it was never built and was considered to be too complicated for the application. The next logical step was to use three crankshafts with three banks of cylinders in a triangular formation and thus was born the '△' or Deltic engine.

Development began in 1947 and the first model produced was the D18-11B intended for use in motor torpedo boats and designed to produce 2,500 hp at 2,000 rpm crankshaft speed for a 15 minute rating; the continuous rating being 1,875 hp at 1,700 rpm. Those outputs were based on a 1,000 hour overhaul or replacement life which was acceptable for that duty, but quite unsuitable for railway purposes. The first engines to be tested in service at sea were

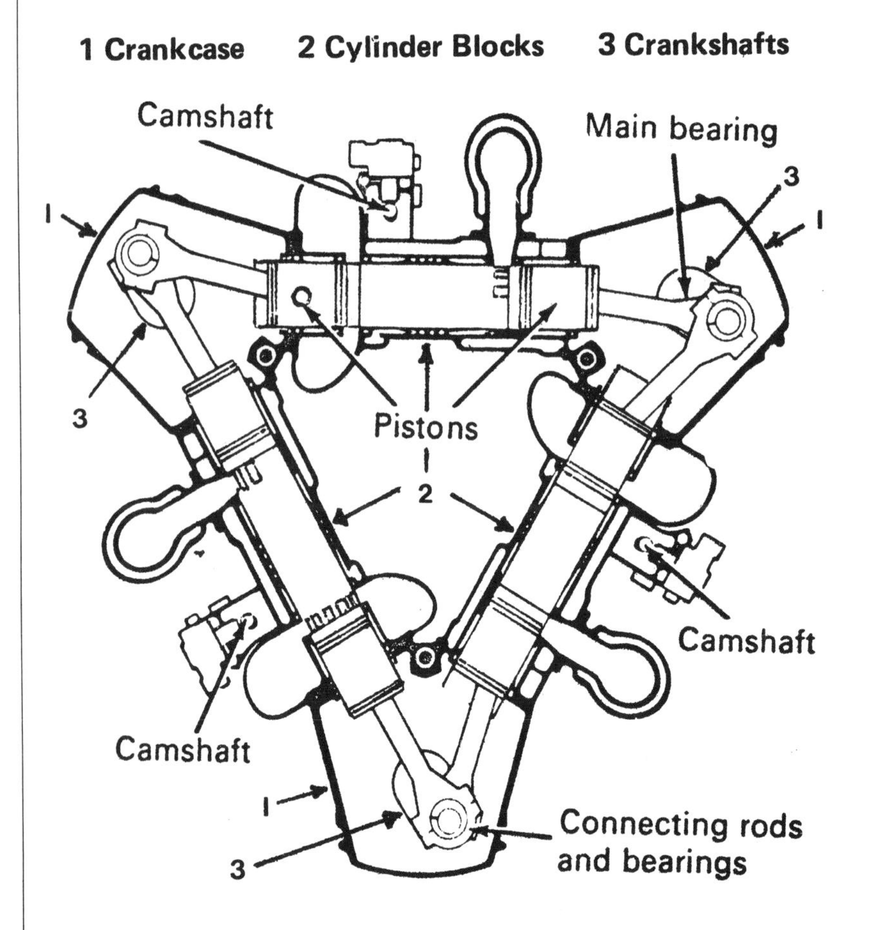

The Napier Deltic Triangular diesel engine, sectional arrangement.

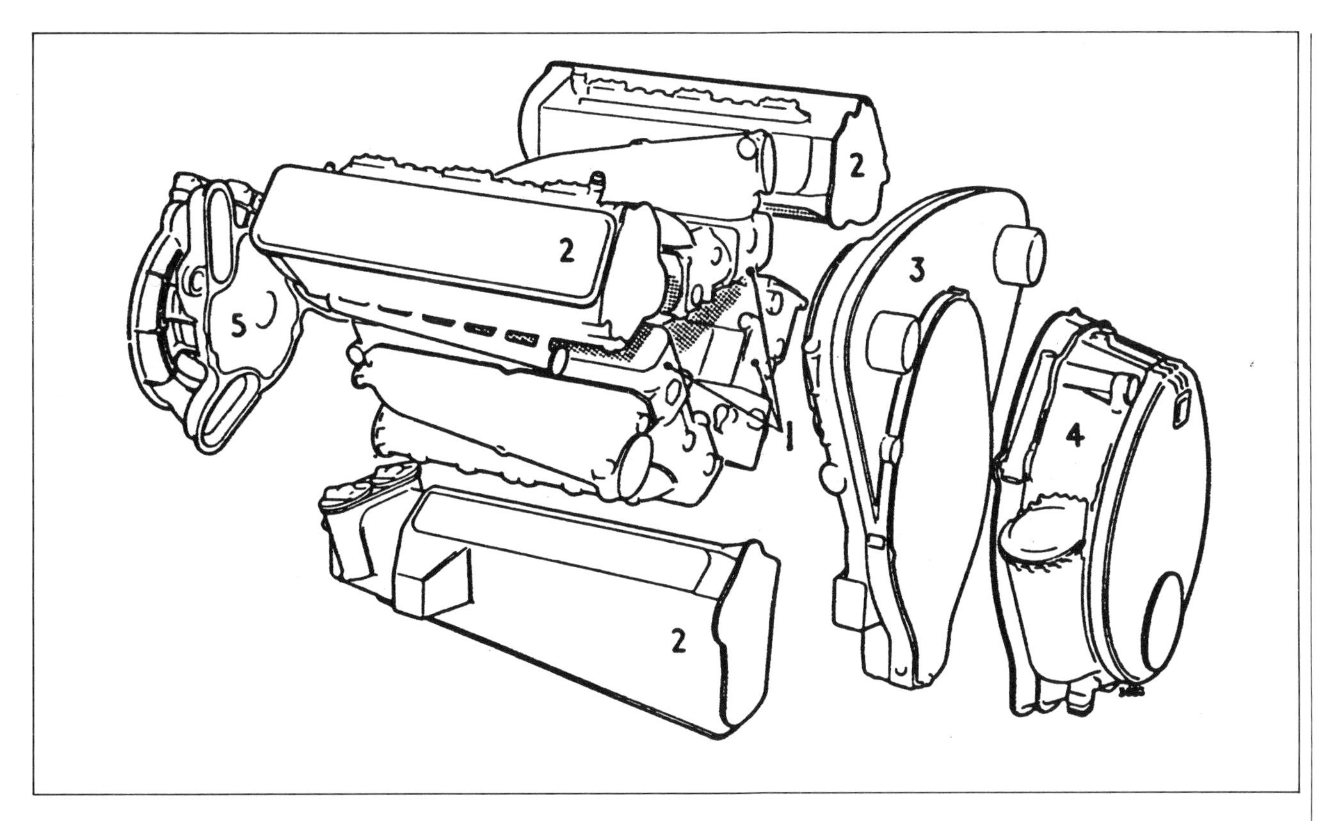

Deltic Basic Components: 1. Cylinder blocks; 2. Crankcases; 3. Phasing gear; 4. Marine gearbox; 5. Scavenge blower.

in 1952 and, as a result of these tests and development work in the engine test house, a suitable output for rail traction was established at 1,650 hp at 1,500 rpm which it was estimated should give a life of 6,000 hours between overhauls.

That model was known as the D18-25 and was fitted with a mechanically driven supercharger which was driven off one of the upper crankshafts and located at the free end of the engine.

The engine assembly consisted of three cylinder blocks and three crankcases connected by high-tensile through bolts which carried the combustion load. Each cylinder block consisted of six cylinder liners, water cooled and machined from steel forgings. The liner bores were chrome plated and had inlet and exhaust ports in which the latter had special cooling ducts so as to avoid liner distortion. The three crankcases were a one-piece light alloy casting, the lower one being deeper to provide a sump for the oil from where it was taken by a scavenge pump to the main oil tank.

The crankshafts were forged and fully machined with a nitrided finish and had six throws with seven main bearings. Each shaft was fitted with a torsional vibration damper and the lower one rotated in the opposite direction to the upper two. The connecting rods were fully machined from forgings and the big end bearings were of the fork and blade type. The pistons were made up of three portions; an inner housing holding the gudgeon pin and an outer body made up of an alloy skirt to which the piston crown was attached; the crown being oil cooled through a drilling in the connecting rod.

Each cylinder block had its own camshaft which was only used to operate the fuel injection pumps since there was no valve gear involved. The fuel pumps were all linked to the engine governor which in the case of the engines used for rail traction was the Ardleigh 303 type, manufactured by Regulateurs Europa Ltd.

The lubrication system was of the dry sump type since the engine was designed primarily for marine applications and had a separate tank from which the oil was fed to the engine components by an engine driven pump. The scavenge pump drew oil from the sump and passed it to the cooling radiators before returning it to the main tank.

The water cooling system in the locomotive installation consisted of an engine-driven pump which passed the water to the radiators which were roof mounted and cooled by a mechanically driven fan.

The three engine crankshafts were connected together through a phasing gear train which was connected to the output shaft for the power take off. The gear train also provided drives for the oil and water pumps, the governor, the auxiliary generator and the radiator fans.

By reason of its design the engine had an exceptionally good

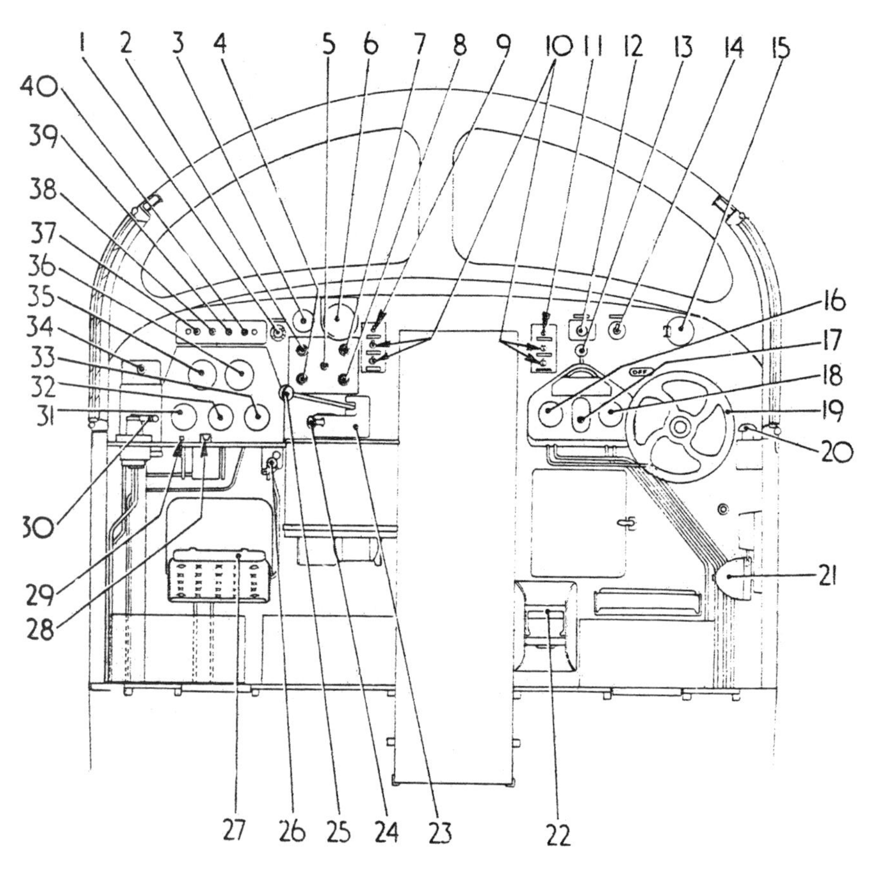

1 Instruments' light dimmer
2 No. 1 engine start button
3 A.W.S. reset button
4 No. 1 engine stop button
5 Earth fault push button
6 A.W.S. indicator
7 No. 2 engine start button
8 No. 2 engine stop button
9 Demister switch
10 Cab heater switches
11 Demister switch
12 C.W.A. boiler shut-down switch (emergency)
13 Water scoop control handle
14 Hotplate switch
15 Pull handle cover (Fire fighting equipment)
16 Steam pressure gauge
17 C.W.A. boiler indicator light
18 C.W.A. boiler water tank gauge
19 Hand brake
20 Deadman's hold-over button
21 Fire alarm bell
22 Hotplate
23 Master controller
24 Reverser handle
25 Main power handle
26 Horn valve
27 Deadman's pedal
28 Air brake release switch
29 Window washer button
30 Air brake handle
31 Main reservoir pressure gauge
32 Vacuum gauge
33 Air brake cylinder gauge
34 Vacuum brake handle
35 Speedometer
36 Main ammeter
37 No. 1 engine stopped light
38 No. 2 engine stopped light
39 Wheelslip light
40 Fault light
41 Main Deltic diesel engine
42 Main generator EE 829
43 Auxiliary generator
44 Fan drive shafts
45 Fan drive gearbox
46 Radiator fans
47 Engine air intake
48 Supercharger
49 Oil tank
50 Exhaust outlet
51 Fuel tank
52 Sanding gear
53 Bogie
54 Footstep
55 Cab door
56 Louvred air intake
57 Horn
58 Windscreen wipers

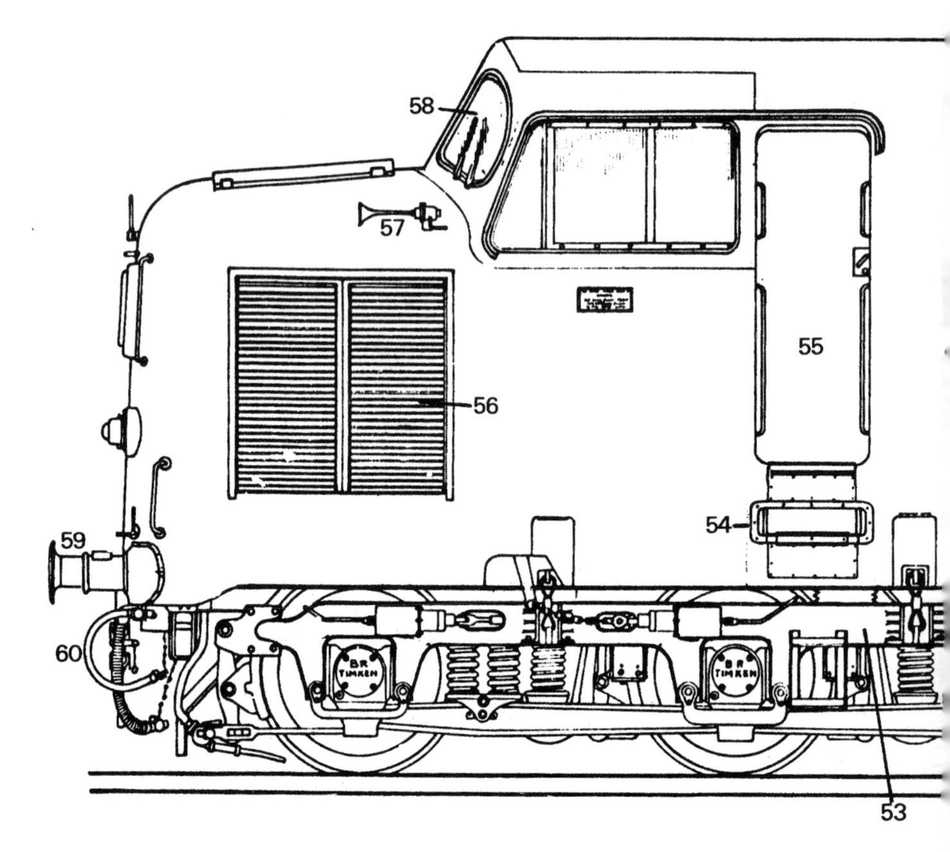

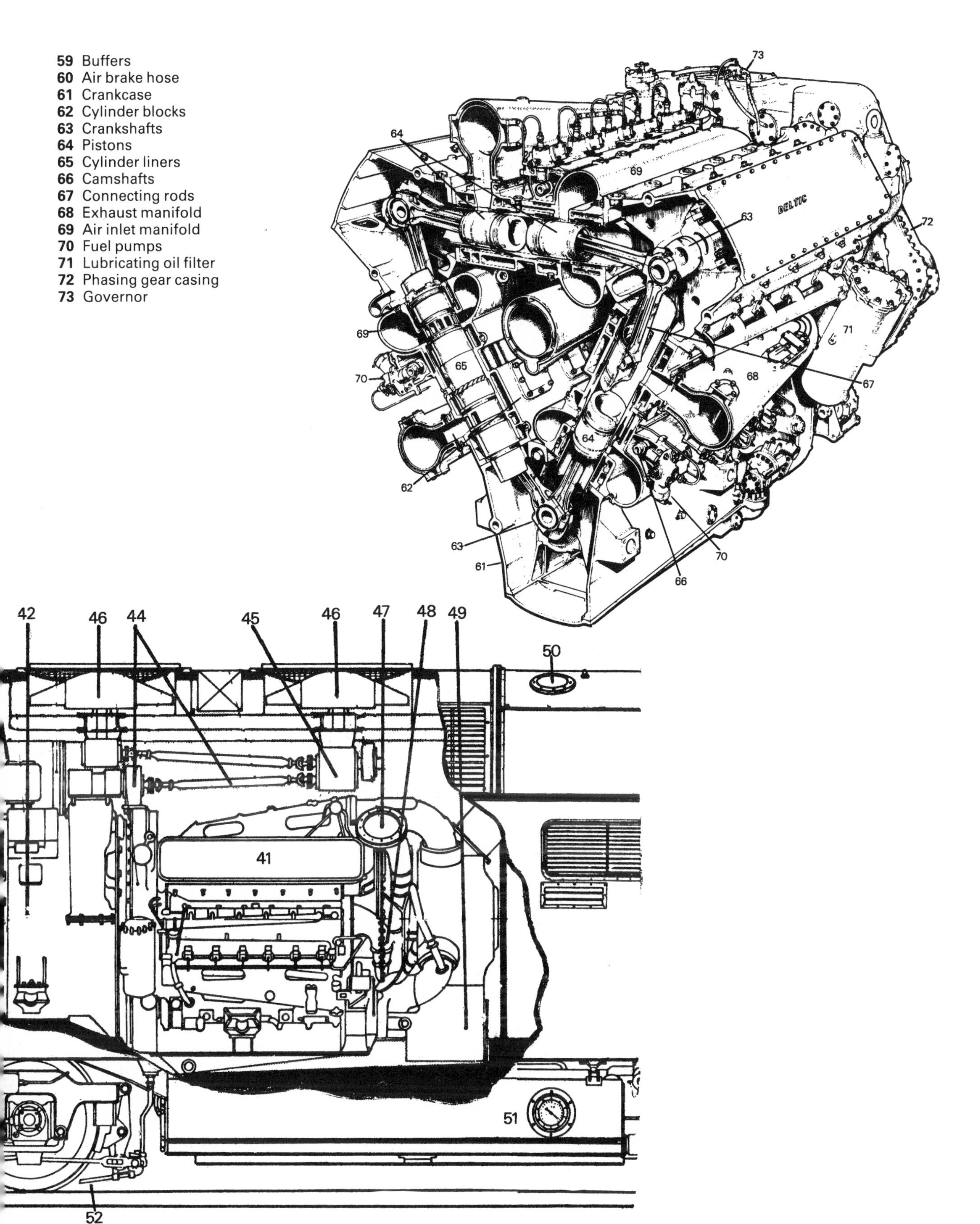
59 Buffers
60 Air brake hose
61 Crankcase
62 Cylinder blocks
63 Crankshafts
64 Pistons
65 Cylinder liners
66 Camshafts
67 Connecting rods
68 Exhaust manifold
69 Air inlet manifold
70 Fuel pumps
71 Lubricating oil filter
72 Phasing gear casing
73 Governor
DELTIC

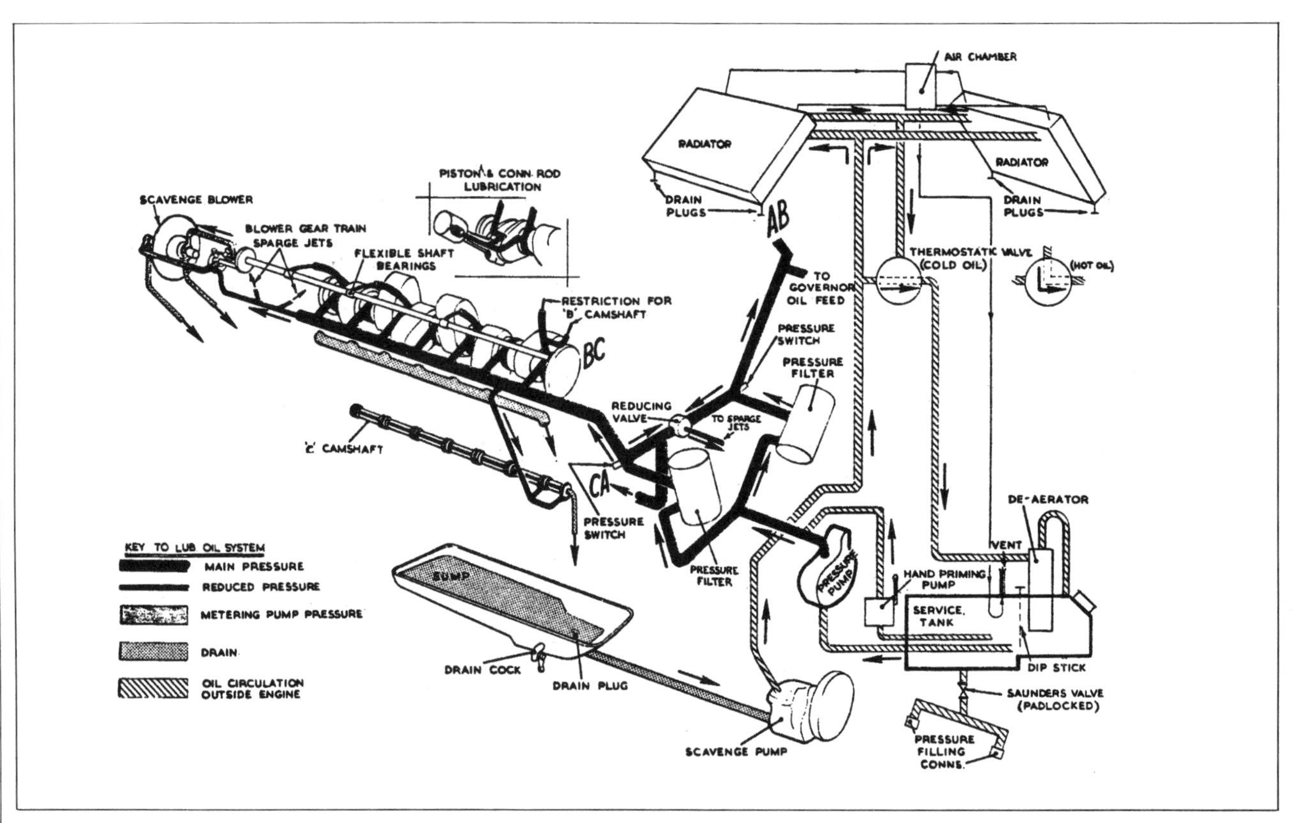

The Deltic engine lubricating oil system.

The Deltic engine cooling water system as installed in the Class 55 locomotives.

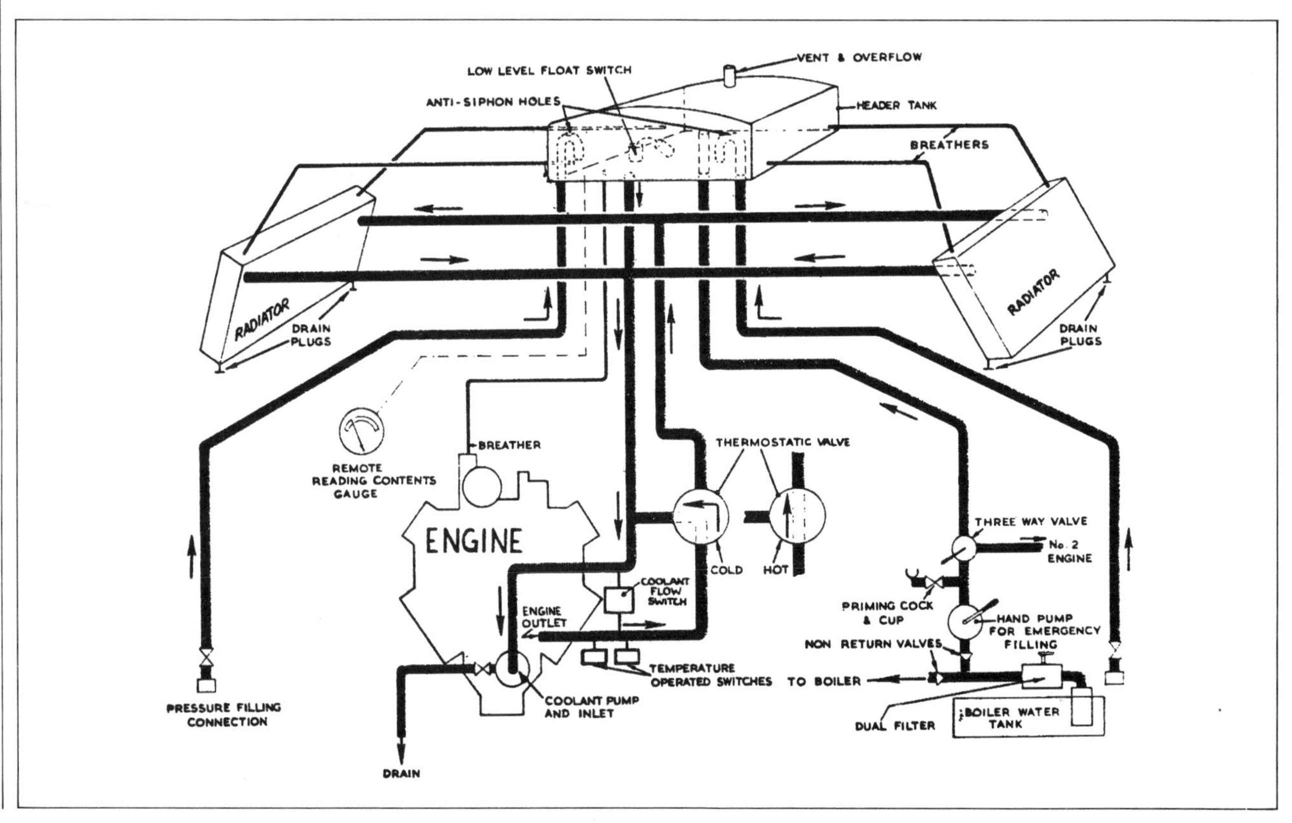

The phasing gear and other gear trains.

ALTERNATIVE ARRANGEMENTS OF AUXILIARY DRIVES

1 Turbine wheel (turbo blower)
2 Turbine drive gear (turbo blower)
3 Blower impeller
4 Impeller drive gear
5 Blower gear trains
6 'A' camshaft
7 'A' camshaft drive gear
8 'AB' flexible drive shaft
9 Metering pump drive
10 'BC' flexible drive shaft
11 'AB' crankshaft gear
12 'AB' crankshaft phasing gear
13 'B' camshaft
14 Governor drive gear
15 Idler gear
16 Auxiliary generator gear
17 Hydraulic clutch pump gear
18 Idler gear
19 'BC' crankshaft phasing gear
20 'B' camshaft drive gear
21 'BC' crankshaft gear
22 Output gear
23 'C' camshaft
24 'C' camshaft drive gear
25 Scavenge-oil pump drive gear
26 'CA' crankshaft phasing gear
27 'CA' crankshaft gear
28 Pressure oil pump drive gear
29 'CA' flexible drive shaft

power/weight ratio being only 6.5 lb per hp for the rail traction version compared with over 20 lb per hp for the English Electric medium speed engine. However, a light engine is a noisy one since there is not so much metal to absorb the combustion noise. Its noise was always a worrying feature for the operator except in one instance which was the New York fire brigade. They had purchased a Deltic engine for one of their engines, and on being told that it was exceedingly noisy they said that, from the point of view of the fire brigade, that was just fine and the more noise it made the better. That was not the feeling of British Rail or the drivers and a lot of work was to be involved to make it acceptable.

As a result of its light weight some of the components were very highly stressed and were destined to give trouble for virtually the whole life of the engine installation. These components were primarily the pistons, the cylinder liners and the quill shafts for the water pump drive. In any two-stroke engine the pistons have a particularly hard life since they are expected to act as inlet and exhaust valves as well as just pistons, which imposes extra loads on the rings and results in their being hotter in the region of the top land. It took a lot of modifications to get the pistons finally right and that was only at the very end of the locomotive's life.

The cylinder liners also have a hard life since the firing pressures are higher than in a four-stroke engine and there is no relief in the form of cylinder head bolts which can stretch momentarily at the instant of firing. The problem of fractures in these liners was to be with these engines throughout their life and was never solved properly. If the designers had had the modern method of finite element stress calculation combined with the present generation of computers, the liners and their housings would have been a different shape and would have worked much better. As it was the engines were to be kept in commission by the Napier team, but it was an expensive exercise, and conditions deteriorated considerably when the railways took over the engine maintenance themselves.

The problem with the quill shafts was not as serious as the other two, but it was a persistent nuisance throughout the life of these engines in spite of many attempts to overcome it. Whether the problem was because of or in spite of the use of splines is debatable, but they were difficult to match accurately and in diesel engines, with their speed and load fluctuations, they nearly always gave trouble at some time.

Basic engine details

Number of cylinders	18
Bore	5.125 in (130 mm)
Stroke	2 × 7.25 in (184 mm)
Cycle	Two-stroke
Configuration	Triangular
Speed range	600-1500 rpm
Mean piston speed	1,812 ft/min (552 m/min) at 1,500 rpm
BMEP (Brake Mean Effective Pressure)	83 lb per sq in
Fuel consumption at full load	0.374 lb per hp-hr
Weight	10,800 lb (4,899 kg)
Length	119.4 in (302 cm)
Width	75.5 in (192 cm)
Height	84.2 in (214 cm)
Compression Ratio	15.1/1
Blower Speed	8,580 rpm

The Prototype Locomotive

In 1942 the firm of D. Napier & Son Ltd was absorbed into the English Electric Company, one of whose important business outlets was in the rail traction field. By 1952 when the Napier Deltic engines were first produced and fitted into high speed naval craft the majority of the rail traction equipment produced by the English Electric came from their works at Preston in Lancashire which had been formerly known as the Dick, Kerr Company. Not only locomotives were built at those works, but also the diesel engines for rail traction and the electrical equipment for both electric and diesel-electric locomotives. This rail traction business was controlled by the Traction Division of English Electric located at Bradford, and some of the locomotives were also built at the Vulcan Foundry at Newton-le-Willows in Lancashire which had been founded by Charles Tayleur to build steam locomotives.

The Managing Director of the English Electric Company since 1930 had been George Nelson, later Baron Nelson of Stafford, and both he and his son H.G. Nelson, the current Lord Nelson, were captivated by the power/weight ratio of the Deltic diesel engine; they hoped it would provide the answer to the problem of world wide locomotive competition, particularly from General Motors. The Electro Motive Division of General Motors who had developed an economical and reliable two-stroke diesel engine, their 567 range, were capturing business from all over the world that had formerly come to the

The prototype Deltic locomotive layout.

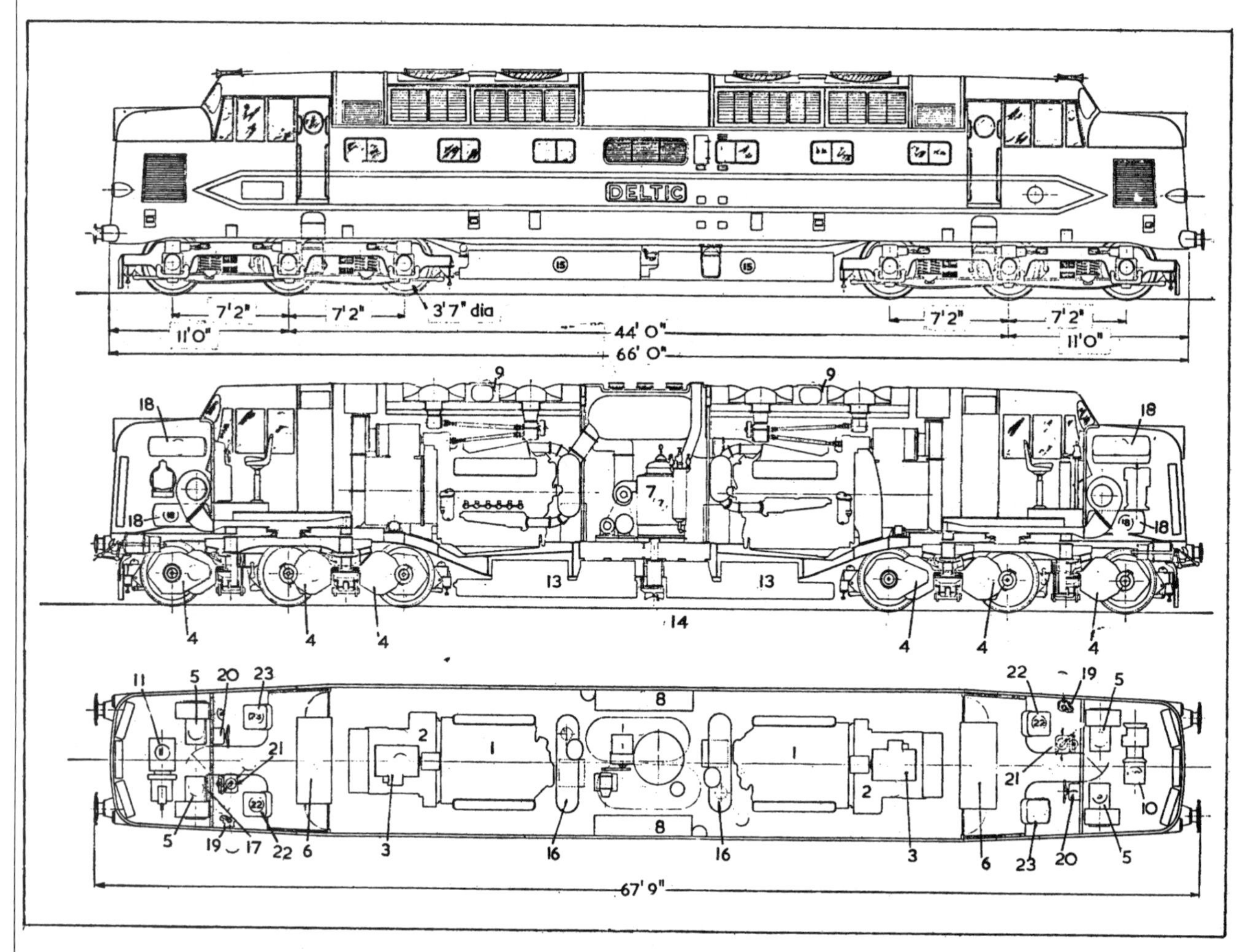

1 Diesel engine
2 Main generator
3 Auxiliary generator
4 Traction motor
5 Traction-motor blower
6 Control cubicle
7 Heating boiler
8 Battery
9 Radiator
10 Air compressor
11 Exhauster
12 Silencer
13 Water tank
14 Water pick-up
15 Fuel tank
16 Fuel pump
17 Air-brake equipment
18 Air reservoir
19 Air-brake valve
20 Hand brake
21 Controller
22 Driver's seat
23 Assistant's seat

The bogie for the prototype Deltic locomotive.

British steam locomotive builders. The British suppliers of diesel-electric locomotives were at a serious disadvantage owing to the lack of a home market, and the diesel engines available were too heavy and were not being developed to a suitable power/weight ratio. That in turn made the locomotives more expensive since they had to have more axles in order to meet the light axle loads of many of the overseas railways.

The Deltic diesel engine offered the possibility of a breakthrough because of its light weight, but customers needed to be convinced that it was a viable engine for rail traction duty. Accordingly it was decided to build a locomotive using two of the Deltic engines; it was calculated that this would provide a power output of 3,300 hp which could be built into a locomotive weight of around 100 tons (101,606 kg). It was thought that there was definite potential overseas for a locomotive of that power, but first it had to be built and proved in the UK.

There was much opposition to the concept within the Traction Division in view of the cost and complications of the engine. One of the difficulties was to design a main generator that could use that power at 1,500 rpm because of the problem of commutation. A commutator is the essential component of a DC machine; it consists of copper segments banded together and brazed to the armature windings from which the carbon brushes collect the current. The design of this component is critical to the performance of a DC generator, particularly one of that power output at such a high speed. It had been suggested that the phasing gear could be used to give the output at 1,200 rpm, but that would have made the diameter of the generator too large to fit the engine mounting flange, so it had to be made to work at 1,500 rpm. The design of the locomotive itself, which was carried out at Preston, was no great problem since the weight of the two engines together was only half that of English Electric's own 2,000-hp medium speed engine. However plenty of those are still being used whereas all the Deltics have been taken out of service.

The basic structure of the locomotive consisted of two box section chassis members which dropped down between the bogies to accommodate the power units, below which was an oil-tight plated surface to prevent the spillage of oil, fuel or water onto the bogies and traction motors. Above each engine, mounted in removable roof sections, were the two sets of radiators and fans for cooling the water and oil. Each engine also had its own exhaust drum and silencer. Mounted between the two power units was a Vapor-Clarkson train heating boiler having an output of 2,000 lb (907 kg) of steam per hour. The main generator on each engine was at the cab end of the power unit and the control cubicle was between the generator and the driver's cab. There were doors each side of the cubicle and a double skin partition, but that was

The driver's cab of the Deltic locomotive.

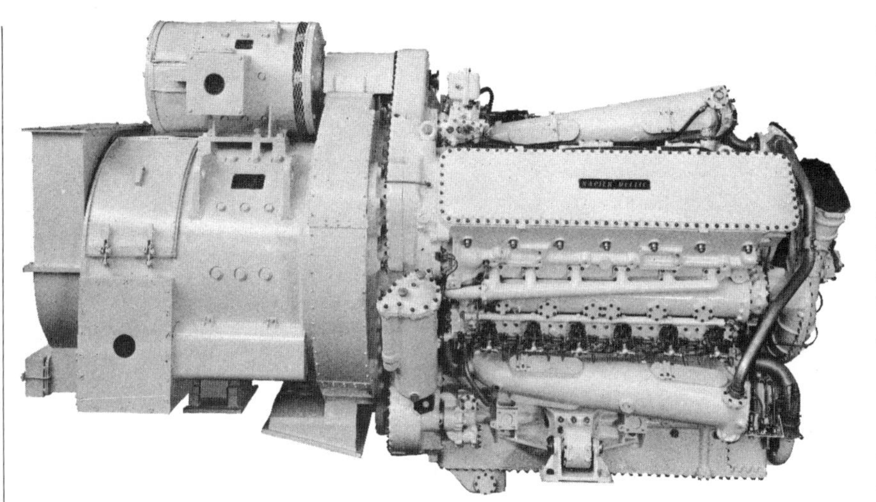

The Napier Deltic diesel engine and generators.

still not proof against the noise from the engine room.

In front of each cab was a nose compartment containing an air reservoir and traction motor blowers; there was an air compressor at one end and an exhauster at the other. Built into each nose was provision for a Tonum headlamp in case the locomotive was called on to do any overseas operations. Beneath the underframe were the fuel tanks holding 800 gallons (3,637 litres) of diesel fuel, and water tanks with a capacity of 600 gallons (609,638 kg); the water tanks were insulated and steam heated and could be refilled by hose or by a pick-up scoop from water troughs in the permanent way. The bogies were fabricated and were of the equalised type with swing bolsters; the load was carried through laminated springs to spring planks suspended from the bogie frame and then by helical springs and equalising beams to the axles. The traction motors were of the EE Type 526/A, six pole nose suspended and axle hung having a continuous rating of 400 hp at 533 amps, 600 volts. The motors drove the 43-in (109-cm) diameter wheels through a single reduction gear with a ratio of 61/19, later changed to 59/21. To supply these motors the main generators were of the Type EE 831A with duplex lap windings, to assist the commutation, and each generator was rated at 1,100 kW at 1,500 rpm and had a maximum designed output of 3,000 amps. The main generators were series connected when both engines were in operation, but in the event of one engine being out of commission the other generator could feed all six traction motors.

The body superstructure was fabricated using rolled steel sections with welded panels while the roof sections and the roof mounted radiators were of aluminium alloy. All air intakes were filtered and protected by louvres in the bodysides. The body interior was insulated and lined with alloy sheeting. The drivers' cabs were well laid out with duplicate controls at each end which consisted of a master controller, a train brake valve and a locomotive air brake valve. The instrument panel contained a speedometer, ammeter, air and vacuum gauges with a panel above showing warning lights for engines stopped, wheelslip and a general fault indicator.

Before the power units were installed in the locomotive they were given a 1,000-hour test in the engine test house at Napier's works under simulated locomotive conditions which included a ducted air intake, exhaust silencers and their own radiators. The only fault that showed up during the testing was due to the fretting of the spline assemblies where these were used on output shafts. It is interesting to note that in his description of the development of the General Motors 567 diesel engine F.W. Kettering remarked that the first lesson that they learned was to eliminate the use of splines. After assembly in the locomotive, the complete installation was given a 200-hour run under simulated operating conditions which included idling, acceleration and deceleration. The only trouble that showed up during these tests was that of erosion damage to the water side of the cylinder liners because plain water was used instead of the 30/70 glycol/water mixture which the engine makers had specified. After assembly the locomotive was painted in blue and grey with yellow stripes and nose flares and carried the name DELTIC on the bodysides. It was to have been called *Enterprise* and had the unofficial designation DP1 (Development Prototype 1), but never carried either of these names.

After trials between Preston and Blackpool it ran to Crewe on the 20 October 1955 and was then allocated to work between Liverpool and London. It was based at Edge Hill Shed, Liverpool, so that the experts from the Napier works at the East Lancs Road could be called to site quickly in an emergency. At first it was used on fast freight work between Speke and Camden since that duty did not involve the use of the train heating boiler which was considered unreliable and likely to cause it to be taken out of service. Also the London Midland Region did not want a locomotive with an unknown record that might break down on the main line. It did one passenger run from Liverpool to London on 13 December 1955 without any problems, then returned to freight duty until July 1956 when it returned to Edge Hill

The Deltic locomotive on test at the Preston Works.

in preparation for some dynamometer car trials on the line between Carlisle and Skipton.

Once the Deltic had begun regular service duties between Liverpool and London some problems began to crop up that had not shown up during the development testing. First, it was found that freight duty did not call for the full output for most of the time and, since a two-stroke engine does not like running at low load, one engine was shut down for most of the journey. That entailed a re-arrangement of the auxiliary circuits so that they could all work off either engine. The ducts taking the air to the engines developed fractures due to the movement of the engines on their resilient mountings and portions of the ducting got into the engines, causing the pistons to fracture. The ducts were then removed, but the air in the engine room was too hot for satisfactory operation and a modified duct with greater flexibility was installed. The pistons also had to be changed since those originally installed had a large clearance to reduce the risk of seizure, but the oil consumption was excessive and unburnt oil got into the exhaust drum and the silencer, causing heavy smoking and carbon build-up. The replacement pistons had reduced clearance and a new type of oil scraper ring which helped to improve the oil consumption.

In August 1956 the dynamometer car trials were

The Deltic near Stafford on the Liverpool-London service run.

carried out on the route between Carlisle and Hellifield which includes the climb to 1,167 ft (356 m) at Ais Gill. The train loads were simulated by means of the three former LMS mobile test cars which with the dynamometer car could impose loads between 300 and 500 tons (304,819-508,032 kg). The maximum load tested was a train of twenty coaches weighing 642 tons (652,313 kg). The results of these tests showed a performance very close to the calculated performance curves with a maximum tractive effort of 46,200 lb (20,956 kg). The calculated performance curve for the locomotive is shown here compared with the measured output:-

Speed mph (km/h)	Estimated Tractive Effort lb (kg)	Estimated Rail HP	Measured HP
20 (32)	45,000 (20,412)	2,400	2,380
30 (48)	33,000 (14,968)	2,640	2,580
40 (64)	26,000 (11,794)	2,777	2,650
50 (80)	20,500 (9,299)	2,730	2,680
60 (96)	17,000 (7,711)	2,720	2,650
70 (112)	15,000 (6,804)	2,800	2,640
80 (129)	13,000 (5,897)	2,773	2,630
90 (145)	11,000 (4,990)	2,640	2,620

The measured output from the two engines was slightly low at 3,250 hp and the losses were measured as 5 per cent to the auxiliaries, 6 per cent in the main generator and 8 per cent in the traction motors, giving an operating efficiency of 82.2 per cent or 2,670 hp at the wheel rim.

With the 642-ton (652,313-kg) load the climb of 1,167 ft (356 m) to Ais Gill was run in 56 minutes for the 47 miles (76 km) with a minimum speed of 47 mph (76 km/h) on the final 1 in 100 (1 per cent grade) to the summit. The estimated balancing speeds for a 500-ton (508,032-kg) train from these results came to 41 mph (66 km/h) on a 1 in 75 grade; 50 mph (80 km/h) on a 1 in 100 and 80 mph (129 km/h) on a 1 in 400 grade. The fuel consumption for the 165-mile (265-km) round trip from Carlisle and back with a 500-ton (508,032-kg) train worked out at 0.8 mpg and the consumption and overall efficiencies at various speeds came to:-

Speed mph (km/h)	Fuel consumption lb/ D.B.HP-hr	Overall Fuel Efficiency
20 (32)	0.60	21.7%
40 (64)	0.55	23.6%
60 (96)	0.54	23.9%
80 (129)	0.57	23.4%

After the completion of that series of tests with the dynamometer car the Deltic had run just over 19,000 miles (30,577 kg), an average of under 500 miles (805 km) a week. From October 1956 it was put onto express passenger working between Liverpool and London on the up Merseyside express and the down Shamrock. In 1957 the workings were altered and it began to run between Euston and Carlisle; this duty included the heavy night sleeping-car trains and in six months the mileage achieved was 47,025 (75,677 km). From June 1957 it reverted to the Liverpool duty with an extra run from London to Crewe and back giving a daily mileage of 718 miles (1,155 km). During 1958 the running was concentrated between Euston, Crewe and Liverpool and in that year achieved a distance of 132,800 miles (213,715 km).

In January 1959 it was transferred to the Eastern Region who were more interested in its potentiality for 100 mph (161 km/h) than in its ability to haul 642 tons (652,313 kg); their main line diesel locomotives which they were just putting into service could only do 90 mph (144 km/h) and they wanted to speed up their East Coast services. On the strength of the Deltic performance they had prepared a timetable based on its potential performance and had placed an order for 22 similar locomotives. It was unfortunate that the Deltic had not been designed to the restricted gauge necessary to work over all the main lines in the UK, since north of York on the former North Eastern and North British systems the loading gauges were more restricted, and the first thing the Deltic did was to damage some platform copings as well as its own footsteps both at Newcastle and at Darlington. That virtually restricted its field of operation to between Kings Cross, York and Leeds.

After a period of driver training and an engine change it first showed its potential by pulling a 250-ton (254,016-kg) train up the grade from Peterborough to Stoke Box summit at 100 mph (161 km/h) with an absolute minimum of 93 mph (150 km/h) at the top of the grade. If speeds of that sort were to be a regular occurrence it was decided that some brake tests should be carried out to test the signal spacings and to see if any of those should be resited. On 5 March a special brake test run was carried out with Bill Hoole at the controls and the climb to Stoke Box was at a minimum of 86 mph (138 km/h). A brake test on the descent to Grantham from 88 mph (141 km/h) required 5,090 ft (1,551 m) to come to a halt, while on the return run a speed of 105 mph (169 km/h) was attained on the descent

D.9021 on a train of Mk I stock in 1965.

from Stoke Box and the braking distance from that speed to a stand was 6,219 ft (1,895 m).

Just after these brake tests the Deltic was derailed at Hornsey and paid its one visit to the new Stratford diesel depot for a bogie inspection. On 21 March it was given a test run on a freight train of 50 cars weighing 1,146 tons (1,164,409 kg) from Doncaster to London, but the run was spoiled by two of the freight cars developing hot boxes; until it had to stop to have the faulty cars removed it had been some five minutes ahead of its schedule. As a final fling before settling down to regular working a special run was made with a four-coach train from Huntingdon to Hitchin, 27 miles (43 km) in 16 minutes start to stop, or over 100 mph (161 km/h); the maximum was reputed to have been 108 mph (174 km/h), but nothing higher was attempted.

From April 1959 it was put into regular service on the East Coast route, but working along with the Type 4 (class 40) diesels and the LNER Pacifics it was limited to their timetable and could not develop its full potential. However, in the second six months of 1959 it ran 56,670 miles (91,199 km) and continued in those duties until March 1961. Then it suffered a traction motor failure having run a total distance of 451,000 miles (725,794 km) and was returned to the English Electric Company's works at the Vulcan Foundry, Newton-le-Willows, where the first of the 22 production Deltics had just left for the Eastern Region.

Owing to the pressure of work at that time at the Vulcan Foundry – which was busy producing Type 3 (class 37), Type 4 (class 40) and Type 5 (class 55) locomotives as well as others for export – nothing could be done to the Deltic for nearly two years. It was finally refurbished and prepared for its last journey to the Science Museum at South Kensington. It left the Vulcan Foundry on 23 April 1963 and, after stopping at Rugby and at Neasden where it was put onto a road vehicle, it arrived at its present location on 28 April 1963.

The prototype Deltic Locomotive particulars

Axle layout	Co-Co
Diesel engines	Two Napier D18-25 each 1,650 hp at 1,500 rpm
Main generator	EE 831A
Traction motors	Six EE 526/A
Maximum tractive effort	46,200 lb (20,956 kg)
Continuous tractive effort	29,000 lb (13,154 kg) at 35 mph (56 km/h)
Maximum speed	105 mph (169 km/h)
Length (over buffers)	67 ft 9 in (20.65 m)
Width overall	8 ft 9.5 in (2.66 m)
Height overall	12 ft 10 in (2.69 m)
Wheelbase	58 ft 4 in (17.8 m)
Weight	106 tons (107,703 kg)
Train heating boiler	Vapor-Clarkson 2,000 lb (908 kg) per hour
Fuel capacity	800 gallons (3,637 litres) = (650 miles/1,046 km)
Water capacity	600 gallons (2,728 litres) = (3 hours)

Deltic en route to the Science Museum, South Kensington, in April 1963.

The Small Deltics

When the Modernisation Plan for British Railways was announced in 1955, the proposals for the provision of new diesel locomotives for main line duty fell into three classes, A, B and C in which the engine power ranges were:-

Class A	600 hp to 1,000 hp
Class B	1,000 hp to 1,250 hp
Class C	2,000 hp or over

As far as the English Electric Company was concerned their range of diesel engines was best suited to fit into the classes A and C for which their V.8 engine (8SVT) produced 1,000 hp and the V.16 engine (16SVT) produced 2,000 hp. The intermediate range B class locomotive could only be offered with a V.12 engine which gave 1,500 hp, but because of its weight, it could not be fitted into a Bo-Bo locomotive to meet the axle load. They could have offered a Co-Co or an A1A-A1A as Brush did, but that would probably have been too costly to qualify for an order. The only hope of getting an order for a locomotive in the B classification lay in the use of a lighter, high speed diesel engine, which meant either buying one from another manufacturer or using the Deltic. Here again the 18-cylinder version was too expensive and gave far more power than was required, but by that time Napier's had developed a turbocharged version of the Deltic from the 18-cylinder type, which could produce 2,400 hp at 1,800 rpm, and they were persuaded to offer a nine-cylinder version of that engine at a rating of 1,100 hp at 1,600 rpm.

The engine, designated the T9-29, was similar to the 18-cylinder triangular model used in the prototype Diesel locomotive, except that it had three cylinders per bank instead of six. The bore and stroke were the same at 5.125 in (13 cm) and 7.25 in (18.4 cm) respectively, the speed range was from 600 rpm to 1,600 rpm and the BMEP (Brake Mean Effective Pressure) was 101 lb per sq in. The other dimensions were:-

Length	86.2 in (219 cm)
Width	68.5 in (174 cm)
Height	83 in (211 cm)
Weight	7,450 lb (3,379 kg)

The engine was fitted with a Napier turbocharger and to withstand the higher operating temperatures the pistons were fitted with a crown of Hidural alloy. The main generator was the English Electric Type EE 835,

The bogie for the small Deltic locomotives.

The small Deltic locomotive as completed.

Prototype Deltic passing Markham in the Eastern Region with maroon stock in June 1959.

Baby Deltic no. D.5901 on an up freight at Hadley Wood Tunnel.

Baby Deltic no. D.5903 at Oakleigh Park with down local of Quad-Arts in May 1965, after the rebuild.

A rare colour shot of prototype DP2 on the LMR near Lancaster in April 1963.

Before naming, Deltic no. D.9007 on up 'Flying Scotsman' near Markham in 1962.

D.9007, named *Pinza*, on down 'Heart of Midlothian' on the clifftop near Bournemouth in May 1962.

Below: Class no. 55.009 *Alycidon* leaving Kings Cross on the 12.45 bound for Hull.

Right: No. 55.010 *The King's Own Scottish Borderer* on an Edinburgh to Plymouth train near Durham in May 1981.

Main picture: No. 55.009 *Alycidon* in June 1983 after preservation at Green End on the North Yorkshire Moors Railway.

THE
RAILRIDERS
EXPRESS

No. 55.022 *Royal Scots Grey* in October 1979 with 'Deltic Pioneer' railtour passing Blaydon.

Under the wires, no. 55.002 *King's Own Yorkshire Light Infantry* at Lime Street, Liverpool, with the 21.15 to York.

Swan song for no. 55.009 *Alycidon* with the 'Deltic Broadsman' special, passing Ancaster in December 1981.

In new blue colour scheme at Doncaster, no. 9010 – the first Deltic to do over 2 million miles – in 1975.

On the last days of its Trans-Pennine duty, no.55.009 'Alycidon' at Manchester Victoria with the 12.05 from Newcastle to Liverpool. Enthusiasts unofficially named this train 'Deltic's Lament' and the engine bears a wreath to mark the occasion.

In September 1981, no. 55.014 *The Duke of Wellington's Regiment* takes a down express over Durham Viaduct.

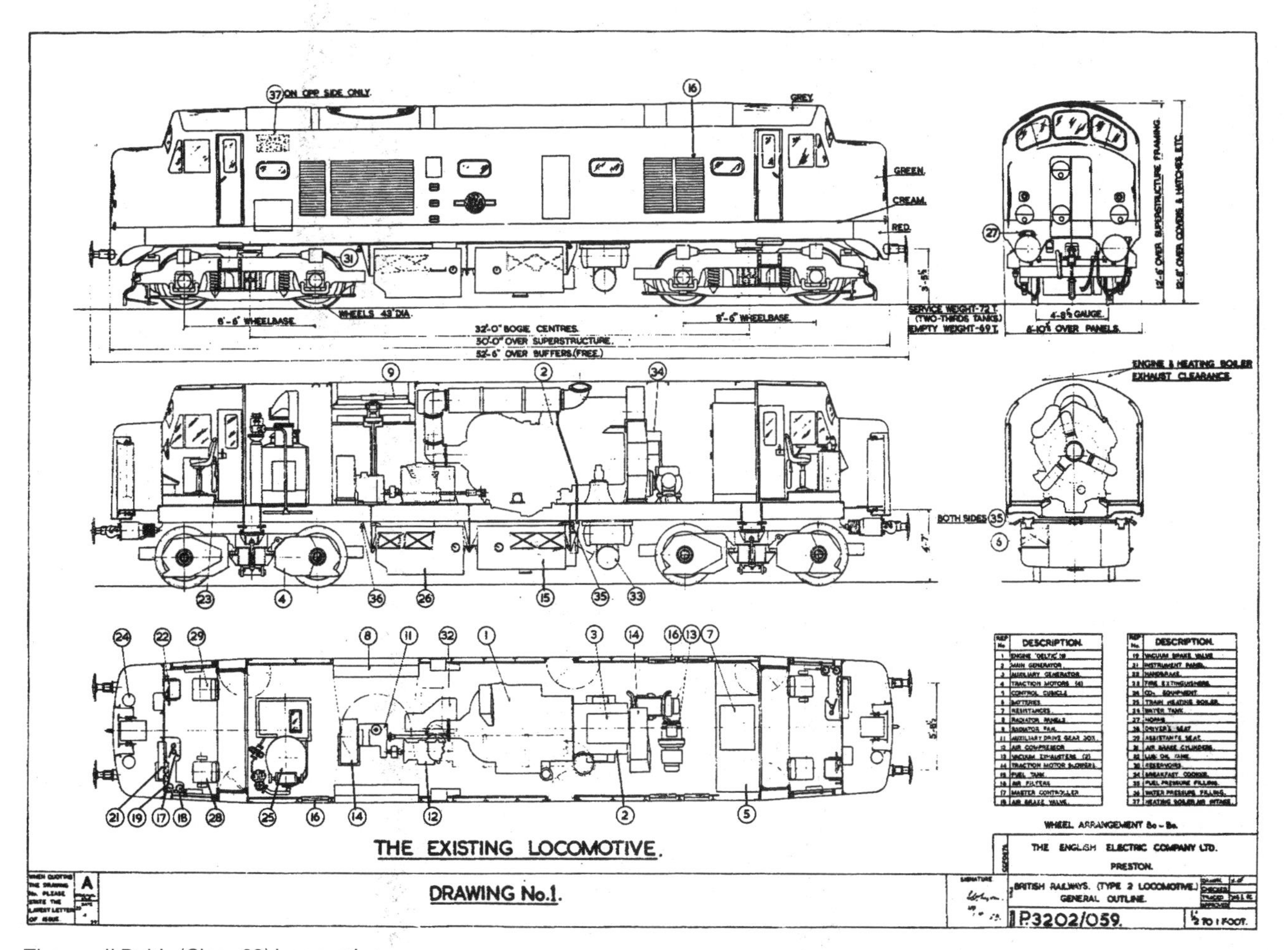

The small Deltic (Class 23) locomotive layout.

D.5907 on a freight train near Hatfield.

D.5905 leaving Kings Cross with a Cambridge train in December 1959.

driven through the phasing gears, with an auxiliary generator mounted above. The four traction motors were Type EE 533A of the standard nose suspended pattern. The radiators for both oil and water were mounted in the bodysides and cooled by a vertical fan driven off the free end of the engine through an auxiliary gear box, which also drove one of the traction motor blowers; the other blower was mounted on the end of the auxiliary generator.

There was a driver's cab at each end with a small nose in front, which contained a corridor connection for coupling to another locomotive in the event of double heading. This was a specified fitting and was a nuisance since it was never used and was a source of draughts in the cab. Behind the No 1 end cab was a Stone-Vapor train heating boiler with an output of 1,600 lb (726 kg) per hour and behind the No 2 end cab was the control cubicle. There was also an air compressor driven off the auxiliary gear box and two electrically driven exhausters for the vacuum brakes. The fuel tanks held 550 gallons (2,500 litres) and the water tank 500 gallons (2,273 litres).

These class B Deltics, numbered D5900-5909, were supposed to have been delivered during 1958, but there was some delay in the engine production and in addition the first locomotive to be completed was four tons (4,064 kg) too heavy. Production of the remainder of the class had to be halted while an investigation was carried out to see which portions were overweight. There was a discussion as to whether the weight of the engine, the transmission or the mechanical parts could be reduced; since little could be done in the case of the first two components, it fell to the locomotive builder to try to lessen the weight. In the case of these 'Baby Deltics' this was achieved by machining metal off castings wherever possible to the limits of safety, mainly from the bogies and their locating pivots in the locomotive body. The frames, the bolsters and the stretchers were all given this treatment and, by persuading British Rail to accept a weight measured with the fuel and water tanks two-thirds filled, the weight was got down to 72 tons (73,156 kg) as specified. They were all finally delivered between April and June 1959.

At first they were welcomed by the Eastern Region who had been unlucky enough to get some North British locomotives with MAN engines and these Deltics gave them the chance to pass the NBL products back to Scotland where they came from, but it was a false hope and it was not long before these 'Baby Deltics' as they were called, began to play up. They were allocated to Finsbury Park depot for outer suburban duties which involved no night duty, so that they had to start up from cold each morning. In warm weather this was not a problem, but in winter the cold oil would burst the flexible pipes running from the engines to the radiators, with very messy results. They also suffered from fractures in the primary exhaust drum and this was a frequent cause of fires in the engine room. They also emitted a lot of burning carbon particles from the exhaust and caused lineside fires in the East Anglia farmlands, which railway officials had claimed would be eliminated if diesels replaced steam in that part of the country. Finally, the drive shafts to the auxiliary gearbox were prone to fracture which damaged the water intake manifold and they suffered from a spate of seized pistons and cracked cylinder liners.

The class remained in service until 1962, putting in about 40,000 miles (64,372 km) per annum, but in that year they had to be relegated to transfer duties because of their unreliability and all ten were withdrawn from service. They were sent to Stratford locomotive works to see if Napier could come up with a

D.5907 on a semi-fast train leaving Hadley Wood Tunnel.

The English Electric 12UT High Speed diesel engine, ready for fitting into the small Deltic locomotive no. D.5901 in 1963.

solution; all this was very worrying because the large Delics were then in commission and it was feared that the same problems might occur in those. Some of them did, but the work done on the 'Baby Deltics' helped in the solution of these problems.

Prolonged test and development work at Napier's produced a design for an improved type of cylinder liner which had better securing at both ends and increased cooling arrangements. A new type of piston with a screwed on crown was also fitted and by the time these modifications to the engines were completed, these Baby Deltics had been out of action for almost two years. Most of them were returned to duty in June and July 1964 except for No D5901, which had been returned to the Vulcan Foundry for the fitting of a new type of diesel engine.

In 1958 the Diesel Engine Division of English Electric had started the development of a

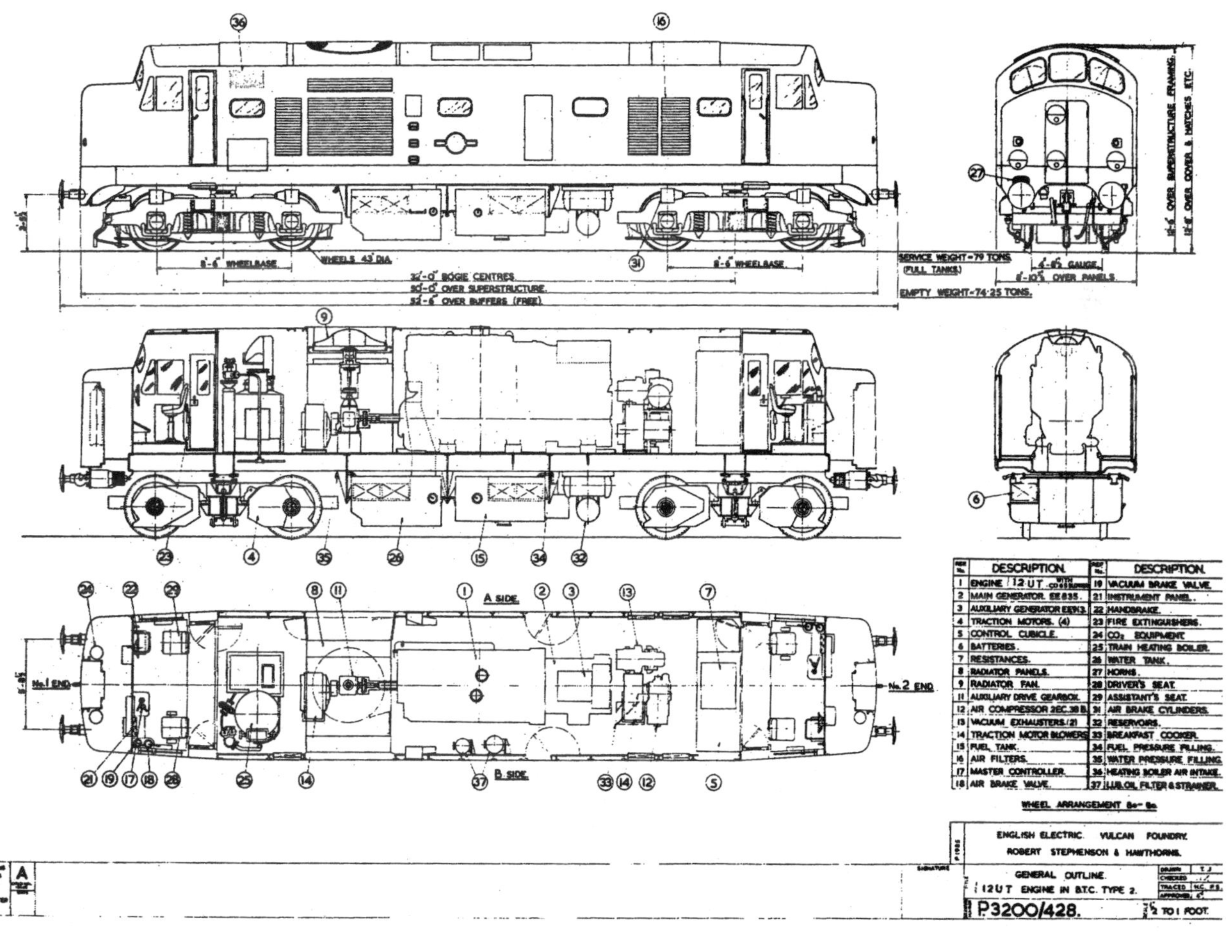

The layout of D.5901, designed to accommodate the English Electric 12UT diesel engine.

The Class 23 under rebuild at Stratford Works in 1963.

lighter, high speed, conventional four-stroke diesel engine, and by May 1963 the first one had been successfully tested at an output of 1,550 hp at 1,500 rpm, with an ultimate intention of achieving 2,500 hp. Two more of these engines were then built with the object of trying one out in a locomotive, and the Baby Deltic was chosen as a suitable launch vehicle. Known as the 12UT models, this was a 12-cylinder engine with a bore and stroke of 7.75 in (20 cm) by 8.5 in (22 cm) and weighed 17,000 lb (7,711 kg) which was 4.3 tons (4,369 kg) more than the nine-cylinder Deltic engine.

Some redesign of the locomotive was necessary, including larger radiators and a relocation of some of the auxiliary equipment, the total increase in weight came to 5.3 tons (5,385 kg). British Rail were willing to accept the higher axle load for trial purposes in view of the increase in power of 40 per cent which would have put the locomotive in the new Type 3 category. The alterations had been completed to No D5901 by October 1963 and it was all ready to receive its new engine when a change in management resulted in the whole project being abandoned. If it had not been for that decision, the English Electric 12UT might have been adopted for the Inter-City 125 trains.

D5901 was then restored to its original build with a reconditioned Deltic engine and returned to the Eastern Region in May 1965. Known as class 23, they performed much more satisfactorily, but because there were only ten of them they were destined for a short life, and withdrawals began with No D5906 in September 1968. Some were to remain in service until 1971, the last being No D5909 which was the only one to be painted in the blue livery, and ran a total of 491,000 miles (790,166 km) as compared to an average of 300,000 miles (482,790 km) for the class.

No D5901 was sent to the Research Centre at Derby in August 1969 and remained in service there until 1976. It is doubtful if these locomotives ever earned their keep, either from the users' or the manufacturer's point of view. Needless to say there has been no preservation society.

The 1,100 hp Baby Deltics Nos D5900-5909
Locomotive particulars

Axle layout	Bo-Bo
Diesel engine	One Napier T9-29 1,100 hp at 1,600 rpm
Main generator	EE 835
Traction motors	Four EE 533A
Maximum tractive effort	47,000 lb (21,319 kg)
Continuous tractive effort	30,600 lb (13,880 kg) at 10 mph (16 km/h)
Maximum speed	75 mph (121 km/h)
Length (over buffers)	52 ft 6 in (16 m)
Width overall	8 ft 10.8 in (2.71 m)
Height overall	12 ft 8 in (3.86 m)
Wheelbase	40 ft 6 in (12.34 m)
Weight	73.9 tons (75,188 kg)
Train heating boiler	Stone-Vapor 1,600 lb (726 kg) per hour
Fuel capacity	550 gallons (2,500 litres)
Water capacity	500 gallons (2,273 litres)

Key to drawing on facing page

1 Control cubicle
2 Resistancers
3 Auxiliary generator EE 913
4 Radiator fans
5 Radiator header tank
6 Route indicator panel
7 Traction motors EE 538
8 Main generators EE 829
9 Lubricating oil tank
10 Water pick-up scoop
11 CO_2 fire-fighting cylinder
12 Exhausters FRU 5¼ × 10
13 Handbrake wheel
14 Assistant's seat
15 Cooker
16 Deltic 18-25 diesel engine
17 Water tank filling duct
18 Train heating boiler (C.W.A.)
19 Engine air intake filters
20 Driver's seat
21 Air brake valve
22 Vacuum brake valve
23 Master controller
24 Traction motor air filters
25 Traction motor blower
26 Toilet
27 Air compressor
28 Exhaust silencers
29 Fuel tanks

The Great Deltics: Phase One (1961-1968)

If these Deltics could be said to have had a conception date it was probably on the 3 June 1957. On that day the English Electric Company handed over to the British Transport Commission (BTC) the first of the new diesel-electric locomotives ordered under the Modernisation Plan of 1955. That particular locomotive was a Bo-Bo of Class 'A', 1000 hp and carrying the number 8000 (now class 20) it was handed over by Sir George Nelson to Lord Rusholme, then Chairman of the London Midland Region of the BTC, at a ceremony at the Vulcan Foundry Works at Newton-le-Willows. With superb showmanship the party of top brass from the London-Midland Region, the other Regions and the BTC was taken from Euston to the Vulcan Halt in a special train of six coaches hauled by the Prototype Deltic locomotive. The start out of Euston station is the most difficult of all the main line stations in London with a one-mile (1.6-km) climb straight away to the top of Camden Bank at grades between 1/70 and 1/112, but the Deltic shot out of Euston like an arrow leaving the usual banking engine idly puffing astern and stormed to the summit in under two minutes. It reached a speed of 95 mph (153 km/h) just beyond Wembley, but after that it kept to the 90-mph (145-km/h) limit of that time; it easily outclassed the pre-war 'Coronation Scot' and it sold itself to the Eastern Region even if the Midland Region did not want such a performance in view of their planned electrification scheme.

Negotiations followed fairly rapidly and by December the following points had been stipulated by Roland Bond of the Railway Division of the Transport Commission as items where the production Deltics would have to be improved on over the prototype so as to be generally acceptable:-

1. Build to conform to C.1 and L.1 loading gauges
2. ATC Equipment to be fitted
3. Braking provision to conform to BR Memorandum of 31 December 1956
4. Cab layout to conform to Type 4 (class 40)
5. To negotiate curves of four chains radius
6. Boiler capacity to be 2,500 lb (1,134 kg) per hour
7. Buffer projection to be at least 15 in (38 cm)
8. Fuel and water capacity to be increased to run from Kings Cross to Edinburgh
9. Toilet to be provided
10. To pass through washing machines under its own power
11. Cooking facilities to be in line with Type 4
12. Wheels and tyres to be to BR Standard
13. Provision to be made for fitting buckeye couplers later
14. Provision for headcodes, lights and train indicator

3300-hp Deltic diesel-electric locomotive layout.

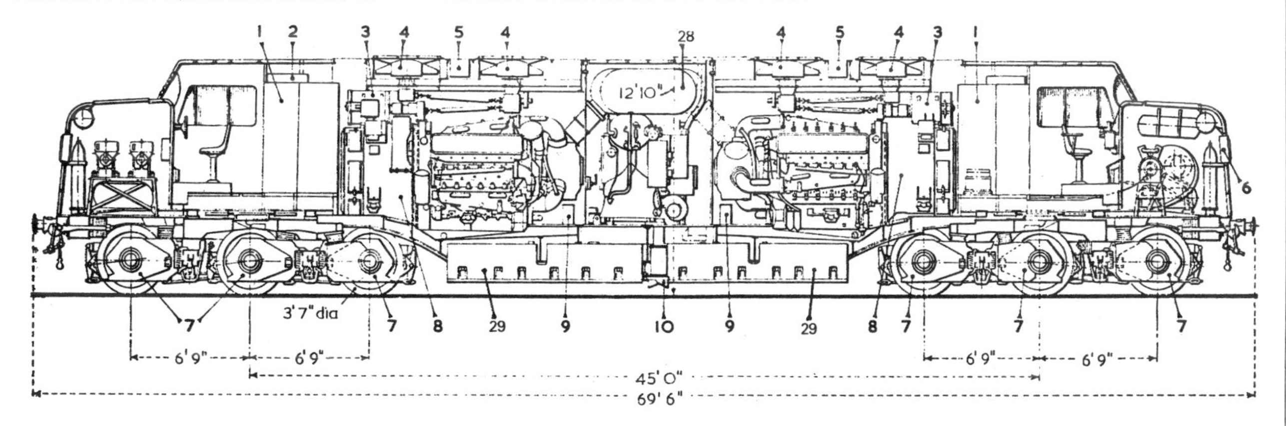

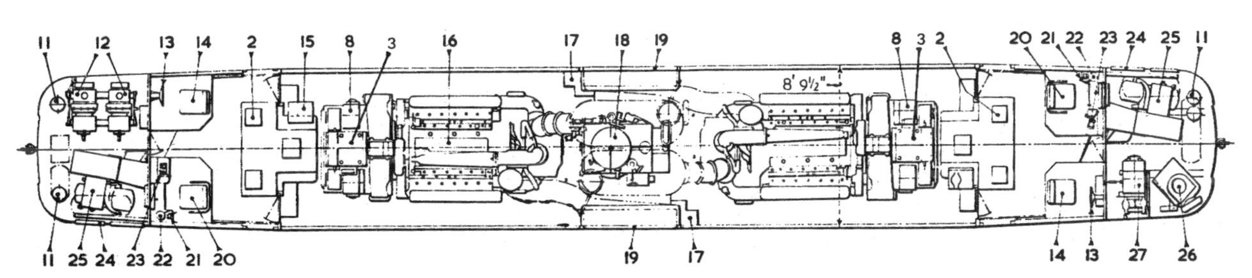

Bogie for Class 55 at Vulcan Foundry. Note the change of design compared to the prototype Deltic bogie. This bogie was also used on Class 37 and Class 50.

Proposed gangway connection for 3300-hp Deltic locomotives.

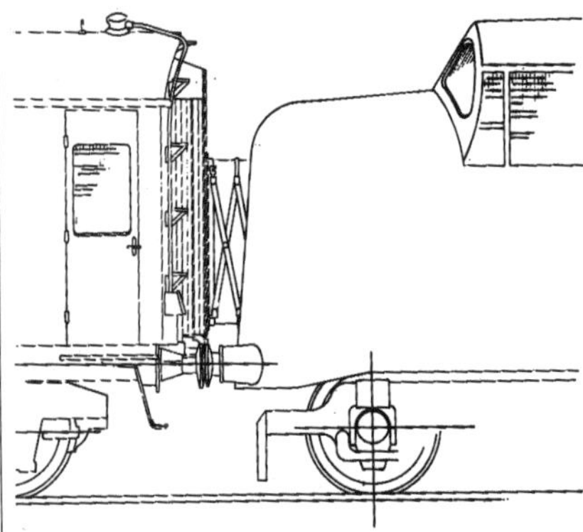

15. Boiler water treatment
16. Ability to accommodate small snow plough
17. Adequate lifting and jacking points

There was also a request for gangway connections to allow for the change of crew members during a long run, but that would have considerably complicated the nose end arrangement and the BTC were talked out of that provision. The English Electric Company pointed out that a spare crew could occupy the other cab in which comfortable seats were provided as well as cooking facilities. The tender was submitted on the 28 March 1958 and the order was finally placed on the 1 May 1958 for 22 locomotives. The English Electric Company had wanted to include the prototype suitably amended to suit the revised specification, but there was too much alteration involved to make it fit the L.1 loading gauge and the larger boiler could not have been accommodated.

The basis of the tender was a locomotive price of £155,000 each (out of which the mechanical parts accounted for £57,000, the two

Locomotive superstructure in building at the Vulcan Foundry Works at Newton-le-Willows.

The driver's deck on Class 55 Deltic.

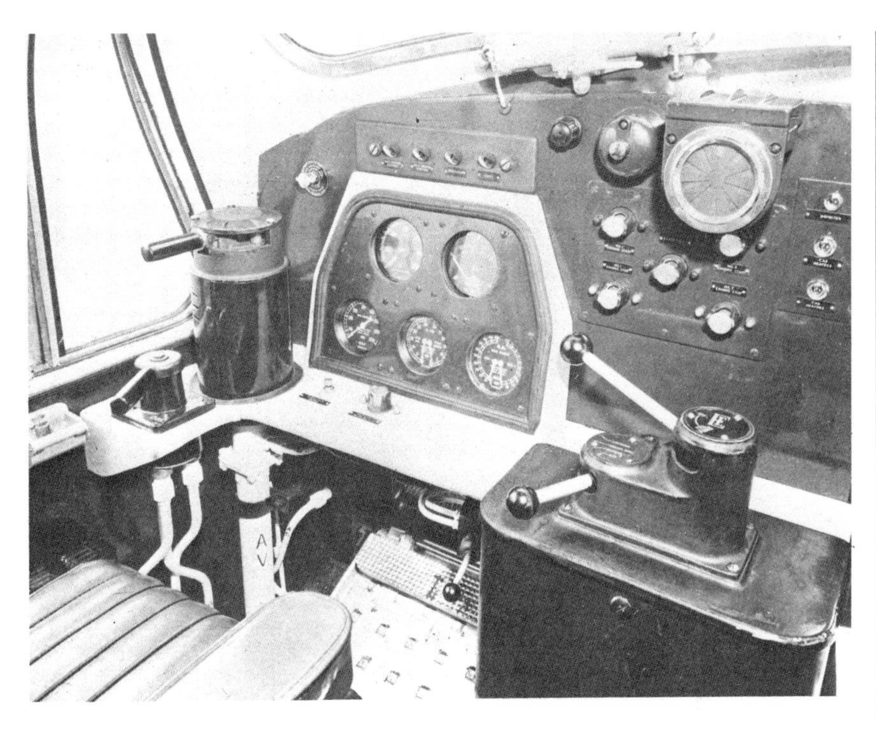

Napier Deltic engines £60,000 and the generators, motors and control gear £38,000) added to which was a maintenance contract by which the manufacturer would provide the spares and service to ensure a fleet mileage of 4.5 million miles (7,241,850 km) per year or 204,545 miles (329,174 km) per annum per locomotive.

These maintenance charges were to be at the rate of £720 per locomotive per month for the first year falling to £600 per locomotive per month in the fifth year with a penalty at the rate of one per cent of locomotive cost for every one per cent of miles lost due to equipment failure. The spare stocks of major components were to be:

3 complete power units (engine and generator)
8 complete Deltic engines
6 complete bogies with traction motors
3 traction motors
1 main generator
3 boiler units

The locomotive design was two feet longer than that of the prototype to allow for the larger boiler and for some of the other points specified and The English Electric Company were worried that the weight would work out at over 108 tons (109,734 kg) which was the 18-ton (18,289-kg) axle load specified in the BR Specification DE/M/3 as issued in February 1958. However in view of the curvature limitation of four chains BR had to accept a bogie design with a shorter wheelbase than that of the prototype so that the same bogie could be used on the Deltic as was to be used on the English Electric Type 3 (class 37) locomotives of which 42 had just been ordered. With a redesigned underframe and the lighter bogies the weight was calculated to come out at 99 tons (100,590 kg) made up of 37.4 tons (38,000 kg) for the two bogies, 18.6 tons (18,898 kg) for the body and 43 tons (43,690 kg) for the power equipment, a saving of 7 tons (7,112 kg) over the original version. There was some controversy over the type of boiler or CWA (Carriage Warming Apparatus) as it was officially designated. English Electric had wanted to fit the American Clayton type which they were making under licence at their Darlington Works, but the 2,500 lb (1,134 kg) per hour model had not been fully tested, even in the USA, and so was not acceptable to BR. Accordingly the choice fell to the Spanner Mk II which was designed to produce 2,450 lb (1,111 kg) per hour; unfortunately it never performed as it was supposed to and was the cause of a lot of the operating problems with the Deltic fleet.

In the redesigned locomotives the underframe consisted of four longitudinal members, the two inner ones being fabricated with deep sections between the bogies while the outer members were made from rolled steel channels. There were oil-tight wells under each power unit with drain tubes to prevent contamination of the bogies, traction motors and cabling. The main frames were tied by seventeen cross members with

The stylist's design for the nose ends of the Deltics.

The locomotive production line at the Vulcan Foundry.

the end sections being designed to accommodate buffers and coupling hook or a buckeye coupler.

The superstructure frame was fabricated from cold formed sections with the exterior panels welded on to form a strong box section. The interior panels were also welded with insulation in between the two skins to reduce the exterior noise level. There were six sliding windows in each side for ventilation, but these were to provide a source of a lot of the trouble with the control equipment. The roof sections over the power units contained the oil and water cooling radiators with their fans and were of light alloy construction; these sections were removable for changing the engines as was the centre section over the boiler.

At each end the drivers' cabs were separated from the engine compartment by a cubicle containing the control gear on either side of which was a door from the cab to the engine room. In front of each cab was a nose compartment housing the traction motor cooling fan and fire extinguishers while in one end nose were the exhausters for the train vacuum brakes and in the other an air compressor for the locomotive brakes as well as a toilet. The nose ends had hinged flaps on top for the removal of the traction motor blowers and there were filter panels in one side for the air intake to those blowers. These nose ends were to be the subject of a lot of controversy over the design and shape of their appearance.

The drivers' cabs were similar to those on the Type 4 English Electric locomotives (class 40), but the engines were much nearer and considerably more noisy so that also was to be the cause of early problems in operation.

The two Napier Deltic diesel engines were of the D18-25 type generally similar to those in the prototype Deltic, but the phasing gear was altered to give a generator speed of 1,125 rpm and the main generator was a six pole machine Type EE.829, but without the duplex windings used in the prototype generator (Type 831A). The generator supplied the six traction motors Type EE 538 which were a four pole type and both smaller and lighter than those used on the prototype, which helped towards reducing the bogie wheelbase and the overall weight. These motors were similar to those used in the Type 3 (class 37) and later in the class 50 locomotives.

The space between the power units in the engine room was made large enough to accommodate the Clayton type of CWA in case it was found necessary to change to that type and indeed it was hoped to be able to fit these in the latter half of the production run; also as the bogies were shorter there was more room available for the fuel and water tanks. The Eastern Region had estimated that the fuel consumption for a through run from Kings Cross to Edinburgh in the winter with full train heating could amount to 790 gallons (3,591 litres) and so as to allow a margin for emergencies, diversions and delays due to bad weather a fuel carrying capacity of 900 gallons (4,091 litres) was requested. The actual fuel tank capacity came to 920 gallons (4,182 litres). The water tank capacity was retained at 600 gallons (2,727 litres) since water troughs were still in use and a small air operated pick-up scoop was arranged between the tanks, facing of course both ways. That feature was only fitted on these locomotives, on the class 40 and on the other prototype locomotive DP2.

By the middle of 1960 Napier was still sorting out some of the problems that had arisen on their nine-cylinder Deltic engines in the Type 2 (D5900) locomotives which had been in service on the Eastern Region for about a year. Some of the items that needed redesign had to be incorporated in the engines for the new larger Deltics and that had held up production so that the first engines were late in delivery. There was also considerable work involved in the production of new drawings for the whole locomotive and the only item that could be used as on the prototype was the water pick-up scoop. At that time also both drawing offices at Preston and at Vulcan were flat out on work for locomotives for export for East Africa, Sudan and Australia and the position had become so serious that Mr J.F. Harrison wrote to say 'I obviously have my doubts in view of the most unsatisfactory performance of the Small Deltics'.

At that stage the Traction Division of English Electric were seriously considering whether an alternative engine could be used, but at that date the only possible alternative was the 16-cylinder Maybach which could produce 1,600 hp and was both heavier and longer than the 18-cylinder Deltic; furthermore the Brush Group had the franchise for that engine and were themselves considering the building of a 3,000-hp locomotive.

One of the features of the Deltic engine that the Traction Division of English Electric did not like was Napier's choice of the Ardleigh governor. That governor had been designed by a subsidiary Company of Davey Paxman and it was not considered sufficiently proven in rail traction for use in the Deltic application. The governor on a rail traction diesel engine with electric transmission has the dual function of controlling the engine speed and power output as well as controlling the main generator output to match that of the diesel engine. The latter function is performed by means of a torque regulator which is controlled by a supply of oil from the governor and it was that feature that was considered to be insufficiently proven. On these engines this device was to be known as the 'Oily Octopus' and the mixture of oil and electrical connections was to be the cause of quite a few operational problems. English Electric had a governor of their own design which had been in use for nearly thirty years, but it was not readily adaptable to a high speed engine and the other most widely used traction governor was the American Woodward type. It was suggested that one of that type be tried out on a Deltic, but there were too many other problems to be solved for any effort to be devoted to that exercise. A little later on the Ardleigh governor was to be linked up with the American Curtis-Wright and the product at first named the Ardleigh-Wright, but that got misquoted as Hardly-Right and the name was changed to Regulateurs Europa which it now is.

During the course of the negotiations after the contract had been placed the question of appearance cropped up and the BR Design Panel brought in the stylists Wilkes & Askmore. The BR Design Panel had been set up in 1956 in order to counter the objections that diesel locomotives looked like boxes on wheels, but that is unfortunately what they are. The stylists spent a lot of time trying to produce an improved nose end including a sloping forward effect at the front and a three-piece wrap around windscreen. Stan Lyon of English Electric would have no part of the latter feature saying that their locomotives were not going to look like Vauxhall Victors and what was more important the gold leaf demisting treatment could not be applied to curved glass at that time. The design finally agreed was the VEE shaped two-piece screen with a vertical nose front. The curved glass treatment was given to some of the railcars used on the Trans Pennine service and these were found to be very prone to fall out so it was just as well these were not used on the Deltics. In some ways it was a pity that the nose end was retained, because it not only wasted space, but resulted in the drivers being much nearer the engines which itself made the cabs more noisy and was to cause a lot of subsequent modifications. Deltic lovers will say that it would not be the same without its nose ends, but they did make the whole body longer and more expensive than it need have been; they certainly did not look all that attractive when they got the full 'yellow' treatment at a later stage.

The Spanner Mk II boiler, the cause of most of the failures in service.

What with the delays due to the engines, the design consultant and to all the drawing office work involved the first locomotive No 9000 did not go on test until 2

December 1960. The first test was a four hour continuous full load run of both engines in the locomotive at the Vulcan Foundry Works at an ambient temperature of 60°F. The peak engine exhaust temperatures were 696°F on the No 1 engine and 627°F on No 2. The locomotive weight came out exactly at 99 tons (100,590 kg). On 12 December a further test of 5.8 hours was run with the ambient temperature artificially raised to 100°F and the peak exhaust temperature was 756°F.

From 13 December to 22 December the locomotive was put onto a 200-hour cyclic load test during which some defects were noted such as leaking oil from the radiators and blow back from the heating boiler when the engines were speeded up. Further tests on the cooling system were carried out in January 1961 and the BR acceptance test was run on 15 February with the locomotive being delivered to the Eastern Region on 28 February 1961. The second locomotive, No 9001 destined for the Scottish Region, was tested and delivered at the same time. The only snag with the Eastern Region job was that one of the drivers' windows fell out onto the track during the acceptance test. The locomotives were officially accepted by the British Transport Commission on 2 March 1961 with certain reservations.

The next two Deltics Nos 9002/3 were delivered during March 1961, but by then the question of noise in the drivers' cabs had become critical with an official complaint from the BTC on 16 March. Some noise level tests were carried out on No 9003 and certain improvements were tried out such as double doors to the engine room and better insulation on the air ducts and on the control cubicle and cab floors. By December 1961 all the Deltics had been delivered except the last two, but the noise problem was becoming more acute with more crews operating these locomotives and at one time pressure from the drivers' Union ASLEF nearly resulted in the whole fleet being withdrawn. A new set of proposals then included insulated panels from floor to roof behind both seats with a heavy curtain in between; in addition an extra carpet of one inch thick Sorbo matting was laid on the cab floor and Revertex panels fitted on the sides of the control cubicle. These modifications were first applied to locomotive No 9015 on which noise level tests were carried out on 23 July 1962 on a run from Leeds to Kings Cross. The noise levels were found to be reduced to 83 dB at the driver's seat and 102 dB at the other one. The difference was accounted for by reason of the lack of a double door at that side of the cab since the cooker was in the way. The previous noise levels had been 92 and 105 dB respectively and these modifications were then approved and carried out on all the other Deltics. The noise in the engine room was well over 120 dB and quite unbearable without ear plugs or muffs; several people had their hearing permanently damaged from going into the engine compartment without ear plugs

D.9001 on delivery to the Eastern Region in 1961 with the BTC Lion logo.

Above: D.9005 on an up Scottish express near York.

Below: The Deltic on the London Midland Region passing Mill Meece, near Stafford, in 1958.

and the noise is more intense than on other engines because of over seventy gear wheels on each engine which produced a high pitched note like a belfry full of treble bells. It was of course necessary to go into the engine room whenever the heating boiler (CWA) required attention and that was not a very popular job at the best of times. These engine rooms could be almost lethal with blowbacks from the boilers, main generator flashovers and possibly a crankcase explosion if a connecting rod came out through the engine side. Preservation societies beware!

The next serious problem to occur concerned the bogies and this first showed up in March 1961 when the transom of a bogie on locomotive No 6700 (the first of the class 37) was found to be fractured. Since that bogie design was the same as those fitted to the Deltics certain procedures were immediately instituted to carry out strain gauge tests on a bogie on locomotive No 9009 to eliminate the weakness in the design and assembly of that portion of the bogie, but by August some other defects were showing up which included breakage of anchor brackets, heavy wear on the traction motor nose suspension and cracks in the main bogie frame members. The BTC stressed that they then had 11 Deltics in service which needed urgent attention so that they could be ready for the winter timetable due to start in September. The rectification work was all completed by 8 September by which time a further two locomotives had been despatched from the Vulcan Foundry, modified to date, so that BTC had 13 locomotives available for the winter service which started on 11 September 1961.

Two further Deltics were delivered during September, Nos 9013/4, two in October, two in November and the balance by 12 February 1962. Some of the later versions proved on weighing to be heavier than the original, the heaviest being No 9015 which weighed 100.5 tons (102,114 kg) with full fuel, oil, water and sand. This extra was probably due to bogie modifications and to the extra soundproofing material round the drivers' cabs.

The distribution of the whole 22 was then:-

8 to Scottish Region Nos 9000/4/6/10/13/16/19/21

8 to Eastern Region Nos 9001/3/7/9/12/15/18/20

6 to North Eastern Nos 9003/5/8/11/14/17

By the end of 1961 there had been four engine failures, one due to the crankshaft gears becoming out of phase, one to a broken connecting rod, one to a fractured cylinder liner and one to a loose gear nut, but the major troubles had been with the CWA. In the North Eastern Region 62 per cent of failures were attributed to that item and the figure for miles per failure was 6,515 (10,484 km) compared to 33,350 (53,670 km) for the Type 4 (class 40) and even on those 33 per cent of the failures had been due to the CWA. By the end of 1961 BTC were threatening to claim damages from English Electric for losses due to late delivery, but Cecil Wade of English Electric cunningly suggested to S.C. Robbins, the Contracts Manager of BTC that their solicitors should get together on the subject and the claim was promptly dropped. In that year the question of converting the East Coast's passenger cars to dual heating, that is by steam or electricity, was considered, but as that would involve the conversion of some 3,300 vehicles the subject was postponed for the introduction of new stock then planned for 1965 onwards. During 1961 there was no improvement in operating speeds, but a trial run by No 9001 with a 380-ton (386,104-kg) train covered the 156 miles (251 km) from Kings Cross to Doncaster in 117 minutes net time with a minimum speed of 83 mph (133 km/h) up to Stoke Box summit. By November 1961 the 17 Deltics then in service had covered 609,800 miles (981,351 km) with 14,508 miles (23,347 km) lost from the programmed mileage due to a combination of operating conditions and equipment failures; exactly how much was due to either was not then calculated, but assuming 50 per cent to each cause the loss ratio for the equipment would have been 1.2 per cent.

On 18 June 1962 with all 22 Deltics in service the East Coast summer timetable commenced; from that date the contract performance mileage was recorded so as to determine the penalty to be paid by the English Electric Company if the actual mileage was short of the target figure of 5.4 million miles (8,690,220 km) per annum. Services were speeded up and the 'Flying Scotsman' at last got back to its pre-war time of six hours for the 392.7 miles (632 km) from Kings Cross to Edinburgh.

During the first year of operation a number of problems occurred including that of flashovers in the traction motors and in the main generators. That usually happened at high speeds when the traction motors were in the final or third stage of weak field operation. It should be explained that once it starts to rotate the traction motor acts like a generator and produces its own back emf (electro motive force) which opposed that of the generator or the electric supply depending on whether it is fitted to a diesel-electric or to a straight electric power unit. When the balancing speed is reached with full field strength a higher speed can only be attained if the motor field is weakened so that its own emf is reduced. On the Deltic locomotives this weakening of the fields took place in three stages, but in the final stage the field strength was down to 30 per cent of its full figure and the motor was very near to the

D.9003 at Marylebone for the 25th Anniversary of the Institution of Locomotive Engineers. Mr Nethersole, the General Manager of English Electric Traction, is at the cab.

limit of its stability. Added to that is the fact that the commutator bars are not always exactly of the same hardness and some wear more slowly than the others thus causing high spots; this results in brush sparking and if the spark reaches to the next brush holder the result is a flashover. Various attempts were made to overcome this problem which included the elimination of the third stage of weak field, the limitation of the main generator voltage and better attention to commutator cleanliness. None of these were particularly effective, but it was found that the problem usually disappeared when the traction motor had been overhauled and mysteriously some locomotives seemed more prone to this problem than others so it may have been due to suspension or bogie riding. Sometimes it resulted in the complete failure of a locomotive, but usually it was possible to get a train to the next stop before changing locomotives.

Bogies again began to be a problem in 1962 with cracks showing up in the headstocks and horngaps so that further remedial action was needed. Consideration was given to replacing all the fabricated bogie frames by a cast steel type and quotations were requested from Usines Henricot of Court-St-Etienne, Belgium who produced the castings for the Commonwealth type bogies used on some BTC coaches and on some other makes of diesel locomotives. These were fitted at a later stage.

The Spanner Mk II boilers continued to give trouble and though over thirty modifications had been carried out including a bifurcated exhaust which Spanners claimed would solve all the problems, their record for reliability did not improve. The complaints from sleeping car passengers were particularly vociferous. English Electric called in the services of Esso Petroleum advice and they reduced the burner capacity so that there was not so much cycling from high to low outputs as that seemed to be one of the main causes of the poor performance. Each transition to high output caused the emission of soot which affected the burner and tended to block the tubes.

The Deltic engine performance remained as for the previous year with one case of dephased crankshaft, one connecting rod fracture and a couple of piston seizures, but the engine hours had increased considerably and the average engine availability for the period August 1961 to August 1962 was 96.3 per cent for a total of 136,541 engine hours; a very commendable start.

There were some other items in need of attention which included wheelslip, noise and draughts in the drivers' cabs, boiler water treatment, smoke emission and engine coolant treatment, but those were problems similar to the many in other diesel locomotives and did not significantly affect the overall performance.

By the end of 1962 all eight of the Eastern Region locomotives had been named after racehorses in accordance with the former LNER system adopted for most of the Gresley Pacifics. The first of the Scottish Region's eight No 9000 had also been named *Royal Scots Grey*.

For the following year to July 1963 the mileage diagrammed was 4,422,965 (7,117,877 km) and the actual distance achieved was 3,651,506 miles (5,876,368 km), an average of 165,978 miles (267,108 km) per locomotive. Of the distance lost those attributed to the English Electric equipment was 386,362 (621,772 km) or 10.6 per cent. The total engine hours were 160,379 which gave an availability of 97.9 per cent and the number of engine changes was 51 against the planned figure of 44. The planned system was to change both engines at each annual overhaul which corresponded to almost 4,000 hours per locomotive.

During that year a number of major modifications were put in hand on the diesel engines while these were being overhauled at the Napier works, the most important being the fitting of a new design of cylinder liner. The features of the new liner included increased stiffness at the centre to avoid cavitation erosion and to reduce the stress in the region of the hole for the fuel injector; the result of that alteration was to reduce the variation in the applied stress at that point from 15 tons per sq in to nine tons per sq in. The design of the seal at the injector hole was

D.9018 on a down express near York in 1962.

also strengthened as that was the point at which all the liner fractures originated.

A redesigned piston known as the Mk IVA was then in the course of being developed to counter the problem of seizures. This was fitted with a bolted on crown and had increased oil cooling volume in the region of the top rings, and it was anticipated that it would give a piston life of 10,000 hours or two engine overhaul periods.

The third engine modification concerned the quill shaft that drove the water pump which was found to have failed due to flexing. That was stiffened up at the centre with a 'ground' finish instead of a 'turned' one, but even that was not really effective since problems remained with that component for the rest of the engine life.

It had been intended that the engines should be exchanged at 4,000 hours to correspond with the annual locomotive operating life at which time it would normally come in for tyre turning. However, owing to the need to keep all the fleet in operation during the three summer months, the overhauls had to be compressed into the other nine months, resulting in a maximum potential average engine life of 3,685 hours per annum. In fact during the 1962/3 period the average engine life was actually 3,645 hours.

In the second year of the contractural period from July 1963 to July 1964 there was a noticeable improvement in the equipment performance; the diagrammed mileage was higher at 4,494,123 miles (7,232,392 km) with an actual distance run of 3,960,683 miles (6,373,927 km). The miles lost due to equipment were put at 180,462 (290,417 km) or 4.5 per cent. That included the removal of one Deltic per week from traffic during the summer months for boiler modifications and as a substitute the English Electric prototype locomotive DP2, then on loan to the Eastern Region, was called in to fill the gap.

That locomotive described in the last chapter was basically a Deltic chassis fitted with the English Electric Company's medium speed 10-in (25.5-cm) bore engine then uprated to 2,700 hp, and during the course of that relieving exercise it ran 43,000 miles (69,200 km) in 58 days, corresponding to an average yearly distance of 222,000 miles (357,265 km), better than the Deltics were putting up. It was a bit short on power, but could keep time if there were no undue restrictions and, being fitted with the Clayton RO2500 boiler, gave very little trouble on that account. The question of fitting that CWA unit or a Spanner Mk III was again considered for the Deltics, but there was not really enough room and it would have proved too expensive, or so BR claimed. The cost was estimated at £4,000 per locomotive and it seems on reflection that the cost would have been amply justified.

The modifications that were needed to improve the boiler performance consisted firstly of a separate air supply taken from underfloor so that it was not affected by variations in the pressure in the engine room, which could be as much as four to five inches Hg. Next the water level in the boiler body was lowered by 2.5 in (6 cm) so that the steam produced was not so saturated. The moisture in the steam condensed in the train pipes and reduced the steam flow down the line. That problem had not been so prevalent with steam locomotives because the steam from their boilers was superheated and therefore much drier. The rate of water feed to the boiler was also reduced for the same reason to 240 gph (1,091 litres/h). A special tank provided water treatment and stainless steel springs were fitted to the water pumps. Automatic blowdown was fitted and the thermostat modified to ensure continuous burning. Finally the control gear was 'tractionised' and sealed to prevent tampering by the uninitiated. As a adjunct the water pick-up mechanism was given a better finish to the machined surface of the operating cylinder and lubricated with molybdenum disuphide. This was to overcome a tendency to be slow in retracting which caused the scoops to be knocked off if there was a set of points just after passing a water trough. The problem of scaling in the boiler was tackled by the use of soda-ash briquettes in the water tanks. This resulted in some corrosion of the tanks themselves and made necessary some alterations in the pipework because the suction pipe was found to be above the correct position and air was getting drawn up with the water or instead of it. All these improvements enabled the boilers to remain in service until the time when electric train heating could be introduced.

From July 1964 until the end of the first contract maintenance period on 21 March 1966 the locomotive performance remained at about the same level, and at the end of the period the total miles run had amounted to 14,092,480 (22,679,028 km) out of which the miles lost due to equipment failure came to 675,000 (1,086,277 km) or 4.1 per cent.

From March 1966 a new maintenance agreement was arranged between the English Electric Company and the British Railways Board (successor to the BTC since 1963) and that was drawn up to cover the repair costs of the Deltic engines only at the rate of 29/6d (£1.50) per engine hour. Assuming an engine life of 5,000 hours that gave a figure of £7,375 per engine which was just about what an overhaul cost. Under the previous maintenance contract the English Electric Company only got about £8,000 per locomotive per year to cover the cost of two engine overhauls which was a very poor arrangement as far as they were concerned. Under the new arrangement the BRB would be responsible for the rest of the locomotive and it was planned that not more than one locomotive would be out of service at any one time which was a bit optimistic. That arrangement was to last for three years until the BRB took over the engine overhauls themselves.

The shopping plan for the Deltic fleet during the winter of 1966/67 was based on the availability of engines as under the previous agreement and assumed that the engine exchange could be completed within the eight hour target time. The proposed shopping list for the period 12 September 1966 to 29 May 1967 is shown in the following table.

Diesel Train Locomotives
Shopping of English Electric Type '5' Deltic at Doncaster Works
Programme for period September 1966 to May 1967

Week commencing	*Annual repair*	*6-monthly bogie change*
12. 9.66	D9021	D9017 (No 1 engine, 441, to change)
19. 9.66		D9013 (both engines to change)
26. 9.66	D9002 (less both engines)	D9012
3.10.66		D9005 (No 2 engine, 412, to change)
10.10.66	D9019 (less No 1 engine, 415)	D9015
17.10.66	D9016 (less both engines)	
24.10.66		D9018
31.10.66	D9020	D9009
7.11.66	D9000 (less both engines)	
14.11.66	D9004	
21.11.66		D9001 (No 2 engine, 422, to change)
28.11.66	D9007	
5.12.66	D9010	
12.12.66	D9003 (less both engines)	
19.12.66		D9011 (both engines to change)
26.12.66		
2. 1.67		D9008 (No 1 engine, 426, to change)
9. 1.67		D9006 (No 2 engine, 413, to change)
16. 1.67		D9014
23. 1.67	D9017 (less both engines)	D9021
30. 1.67	D9013 (less both engines)	
6. 2.67	D9012 (less No 1 engine, 443)	
13. 2.67		D9002 (No 1 engine, 419, to change)
20. 2.67	D9005	D9019
27. 2.67	D9015 (less both engines)	
6. 3.67		D9016 (both engines to change)
13. 3.67	D9018 (less both engines)	D9020
20. 3.67		
27. 3.67	Easter Monday D9009 (less both engines)	
3. 4.67		D9000 (both engines to change)
10. 4.67	D9001 (less both engines)	D9004
17. 4.67		D9007
24. 4.67	D9011 (less both engines)	D9010
1. 5.67		D9003 (both engines to change)
8. 5.67	D9008	
15. 5.67	D9006 (less both engines)	
22. 5.67	D9014	
29. 5.67	Whit Monday	

Chief Mechanical & Electrical Engineer,
Eastern Region, DONCASTER.

A Deltic-hauled down express near Welwyn North Tunnel.

By 1966 a considerable number of main line services were being speeded up, with 10 minutes or more being saved between Kings Cross and Doncaster, although the ride with the Mk I coaches then in service left a lot to be desired. Steam locomotives were being withdrawn rapidly and by the end of 1965 there were only 153 steamers in the Eastern Region and 493 in the North Eastern Region.

During 1966 plans were put in hand to convert the Deltics to handle the new Mk II coaching stock fitted with compressed air brakes due in 1968, and, since the existing Worthington-Simpson air compressor could not cope with the demands of a complete train, it was replaced by two Davies & Metcalf compressors designed to run at 1,250 rpm, but actually used at 1,000 rpm to give a total output of 60 cu ft of air per minute. After some controversy it was found that the auxiliary generator and its drive could cope with the extra demand. The change-over to air braking was achieved between November 1967 and July 1968.

During 1967 consideration was given to the fitting of an electronic wheelslip detector and a system proposed by Brush Company was tried out on five locomotives. It was intended to equip all the Deltics since they were prone to

The first BTC crest of 1948.

The second BR crest of 1956.

The current BR logo.

wheelslip, which not only reduced their performance potential, but could produce dangerous rail burns. The production versions of these detectors did not come up to expectations because of unreliable current transducers and all the equipment had to be removed.

Since electronics were becoming the fashion and were being tried on all sorts of railway equipment, a price was worked out for replacing the oil operated torque regulators with static load regulators, but the costs proved too high to be justified. That year the prototype DP2 was fitted with just this equipment and was doing fine when it was wrecked in an accident at Thirsk on the main line.

The question of electric train heating (ETH) was also investigated during 1967 together with the whole issue of preparing the Deltic fleet for a further ten years of life from the point of view of the electrical equipment. On most of the other diesel-electric locomotives a dual-wound alternator was to be fitted to the main generator in place of the co-axial auxiliary generator, but on the Deltic power unit with its saddle-mounted auxiliary generator that was not possible. The scheme to be adopted was to use the main generators themselves and this will be described in the next chapter.

By way of comparison, some figures quoted by the Scottish Region for costs for Deltic and Brush C (class 47) 2,750 hp engines gave the relative figures at:-

	Deltic	**Class 47**
Annual depot cost per loco	£4,575	£2,711
Annual works cost per loco	£37,175	£6,934
Total cost per mile	6/- (30p)	1/8d (8p)

By 1968 all the Deltics had been repainted in the new blue colour scheme with the new BR double arrow logo which was the third one to be adopted. In a way they were symbolic of their time in that the first crest to be adopted after nationalisation was the 'Hungry Lion' which lasted until 1956 and epitomised the period when the wheel carried the British public and the system paid for itself. The second version adopted in 1956 at the start of the Modernisation Scheme was applied to the Deltics at their inception and in that the Lion carried the wheel and the Railways were carried by the taxpayer. In the final and current version some unkind folk say that this symbolises a lack of clear direction and that the system does not know where it is going; perhaps there is a better one to come at some future date.

Deltic locomotive specification

Axle layout	Co-Co
Diesel engines	Two Napier D18-25 1,650 hp at 1,500 rpm
Main generator	EE 829 running at 1,125 rpm
Traction motors	Six EE 538A
Wheel diameter	43 in (109 cm)
Maximum tractive effort	50,000 lb (22,680 kg)
Continuous tractive effort	30,500 lb (13,835 kg) at 32 mph (52 km/h)
Maximum speed	103 mph (166 km/h)
Length (over buffers)	69 ft 6 in (21 m)
Width (overall)	8 ft 9½ in (2.66 m)
Height (overall)	12 ft 10 in (3.91 m)
Wheelbase	58 ft (17.6 m)
Weight	99 tons (100,590 kg)
CWA	Spanner Mk II 2,450 lb/hr (1,111 kg/h)
Compressor	Worthington-Simpson MSV 38
Exhausters	Two Davies & Metcalf FRU 5¼ × 10
Fuel tank capacity	920 gallons (4,182 litres)
Water tank capacity	640 gallons (2,909 litres)
After conversion to ETH and air braking	
Fuel tank capacity	826 gallons (3,755 litres)
Water tank capacity	830 gallons (3,773 litres)
Air compressors	Two Davies & Metcalf

The Great Deltics: Phase Two-Class 55 (1969-1981)

With the cessation of all steam working in 1968, and with proposals for the Advanced Passenger Train and the High Speed Train being actively pursued, the accent was all on achieving a modern high speed rail network. The vacuum brake and steam heating were on the way out at last and plans were afoot to modernise the whole East Coast route with 100 mph (161 km/h) operation for 240 miles (386 km) out of the 268 miles (431 km) to Newcastle. Although the East Coast line was much easier physically than its Western rival, with an altitude of no more than 305 ft (93 m) at Stoke Box, it still had a number of speed restrictions, the worst of which were 20 mph (32 km/h) through Peterborough, 60 mph (96 km/h) through Newark and Doncaster, 45 mph (72 km/h) at the Selby Swing bridge, 25 mph (40 km/h) through the York curve and 30 mph (48 km/h) at Durham and at the approach to Newcastle over the Tyne bridge. By 1973, with the first phase of the improvement plan, these limits had been raised to 100 mph (161 km/h) at Peterborough, 80 mph (129 km/h) at Newark, 60 mph (96 km/h) at Selby and 75 mph (120 km/h) through Durham thereby knocking twenty minutes off the times to Doncaster and thirty minutes to Newcastle. During 1968 the Eastern Region (which included the North Eastern Region) received over 200 Mk II coaches with air braking and dual heating, all fitted with the new B4 bogie which gave a much better ride and enabled a further speed up in services.

The next major feature in the Deltic life cycle was the conversion to electric train heating (ETH) in preparation for a further supply of Mk IId stock in 1970/1 which was to be fully air conditioned whereas the earlier stock only had pressure ventilation. As mentioned in the previous chapter the usual method of ETH could not be applied to the Deltics because there was insufficient room either above the main generator or at the ends to accommodate the train heating generator; also that would have had to be large enough to heat the whole train from either engine in case one was out of action. There might have been room if the CWA boiler had been removed, but that had to be kept in use for heating the overnight sleeping cars and postal vans, which were not due to be converted to dual heating.

In December 1967 English Electric submitted a scheme for a general overhaul of these locomotives combined with a modernisation scheme. This scheme included a tractive effort control similar to the one then being tested on the DP2 prototype; a new KV10 thyristor load regulator; modification of the main generators to provide a droop characteristic; a static voltage regulator and wheelslip control similar to that being fitted to the new class 50 (2,700-hp) locomotives then being built. At the same time a rehabilitation of the bodywork and mechanical parts was proposed which included radiators, fan drive gear boxes, control cubicles, cabling and pipework. The estimated cost of the total work amounted to £25,000 per locomotive.

For the ETH scheme it was proposed to use the main generators as was done on the diesel-electric railcars supplied to the Southern Region in 1957 by English Electric and which had proved completely successful. The difference between these units and the Deltic installation was that on the Southern units each power car, which had an engine of 5/600 hp, supplied the heat to only three coaches whereas the Deltics would be expected to heat a ten coach train with a total heat load of 165 kW (almost 250 hp). The two main generators in the Deltic were coupled in series so that the total output voltage could vary between zero and 1,800 volts. That was quite unsuitable for the heating load which required a fairly steady

55013 'The Black Watch' of the Scottish Region at Newcastle in November 1977.

55007 'Pinza' on the 10.05 from Kings Cross leaving Selby with a train of Mk II stock in June 1979.

input in the region of 800 volts. The problem was overcome by arranging for the heating to be supplied first from both power units when they were idling with full field excitation but, as soon as the driver moved the controller to a power notch, the heating load was transferred to one generator on which the power output was increased at a greater rate than on the other. When the total load demand was 1,000 hp, one engine was giving 200 hp while the one with the heating load was producing 800 hp. At 2,000 hp the engine outputs were 400 and 1,600 hp respectively and above 2,000 hp the lower output unit rapidly caught up with the other so that they were both equal at the full load demand.

The layout was also arranged so that on reversal of the locomotive the heating load was transferred to the other engine in order to equalise the loading cycles on the two engines. As at first arranged the heating supply was not available if one power unit was out of action, but there were objections to that arrangement and the layout was modified to allow the train to be heated even if only one engine was working and the loss of traction power had to be accepted. The latter modification was first applied to locomotive No D9016 which had a three-position switch fitted in the No 2 cubicle; that was not carried out until 1973. There was the problem of where to accommodate the additional control equipment for the ETH exercise in a locomotive already brimful of equipment but luckily, as part of the refurbishing scheme, some alterations were made in the control circuits to the six traction motors. In the revised scheme each pair of motors was rearranged to share the weak field contactors and reversers instead of having one set for each motor. That modification allowed sufficient room in the No 2 cubicle for the ETH gear.

The rearrangement of traction motor circuitry also allowed for the fitting of a voltage balance system across each pair of motors which acted as wheelslip detection and prevention device. That arrangement proved only slightly more effective than the previous one in which the current used by each motor was measured against that of other motors, either of which could have been a false basis for comparison. An indication of the problem was that in 1969 one report mentioned that even in May No D9005 lost 16 minutes between Leeds and Wakefield one morning due to wheelslip, and that No D9010 could only make 5 mph (8 km/h) over Geldred Viaduct aided by linesmen throwing ashes from the embankment under the wheels.

Finally as part of the ETH exercise the water scoops were removed, since there were no troughs left in service and additional water capacity was provided for the overnight trains. That had to be done at the expense of some fuel capacity and, in the final arrangement, the fuel tanks were reduced to 826 gallons (3,755 litres) (a loss of 94 gallons/427 litres) and the water capacity was increased by 190 gallons (864 litres) to 830 gallons (3,773 litres).

Before the ETH exercise was carried out there was a major upheaval in the system of engine overhauls. The final outcome was a rearrangement of the diesel engine manufacturing location, in which the medium speed engines were all made at the Vulcan Foundry Works at Newton-le-Willows and the high speed engines at the Paxman Works at Colchester. That involved the transfer of the Ruston engines from Lincoln to Newton and the adoption of the Ruston name for the products from those works, thus the former English Electric rail traction engines became known as the Ruston RK range. Simultaneously the Napier Deltic engines were transferred from Liverpool to Colchester where they are now known as Paxman Deltics. Since practically none of the Napier people would go to Colchester the maintenance work could not be continued and English Electric, shortly to be taken over by the General Electric Company, intimated to BR that it could not continue with the overhaul arrangements. From 1969 therefore, the overhaul was transferred to the BR works at Doncaster and, according to Mr R.J. Smith the current Chairman of the Deltic Preservation Society, taking over that repair work was one of the most difficult tasks ever undertaken by British Railways Engineering Ltd.

The BR personnel from Doncaster were given courses at the Napier works and allowed to visit the naval base near Portsmouth, the only place outside the Napier works where Deltic engines were repaired. There was considerable co-operation on the

55022 'Royal Scots Grey' at Wreay on the London Midland West Coast main line with Deltic Pioneer Railtour in October 1979.

part of the engine builders who offered to undertake some engine repairs to tide Doncaster over the first few months, but that co-operation was nearly ruined by an unfortunate letter from the Supplies Manager of BR who tried to pin English Electric down to a tight financial arrangement and nearly upset the whole amicable arrangement.

Doncaster had undertaken some overhaul work on the nine cylinder engines for the class 23 'Baby Deltics', but the first 18-cylinder engine overhauled was described as a complete disaster and by 1971 the position was so bad that a total of 11 locomotives were in shops. The position was not quite as bad as it might have been, since the timetable had been adjusted to take account of the extra locomotives being out of service for the fitting of the ETH and for the slight loss of power that this would entail, so that schedules could be met by the use of class 47 locomotives. Apart from the necessity to learn the techniques involved in the repair of such a precision-built engine, the works were not under a penalty contract as Napier had been and there was not the same pressure to produce the required quantity of replacement engines.

In 1970, the first full year of operation after Doncaster took over the engine repairs, there were 77 engine withdrawals above those planned and in one week alone there were 11 failures due to cracked cylinder liners. An analysis of engine performance for that year showed an average engine life of 4,192 hours for engines repaired by Napier and 2,722 hours for those overhauled at Doncaster. BREL were finding that engine overhaul was not such an easy job as they thought it would be, which led to the setting up of a team to analyse the root causes of these failures.

The two most troublesome features of the engine were found to be the cylinder liners and the pistons. The engines were some ten years old by this time and originally had run with the first pattern of thin wall liners which had caused some fretting in the cylinder blocks. The seals on the liners were a problem because they leaked, causing loss of cooling water which led to overheating and this in turn aggravated the other problem, the fracture of the liners at the injector hole.

The sealing problem was overcome eventually by the use of a stronger liner known as the Type 42K which was held in position by a ring nut; that was the last of four types of liner to be tried out; various sealing methods were tried out in the two other types, one using a nitrile ring and one using a spring loaded land, but were not very successful. As far as pistons were concerned most of the engines at that date were fitted with the Mk III version which had a screwed on crown, but a Mk IV version was still under development and due for trial in service.

One result of the fitting of the ETH was that when the Mk IId coaches (equipped with a motor alternator set for the air conditioning) were attached to a Deltic, the overload relay tripped when the alternator set was started up. Since the set took a starting current of 375 amps the overload relay had to be set up to 900 amps and the trouble was cured. One major benefit of the ETH scheme was that the power application on starting from a station was much smoother since one engine speeded up in advance of the other and that eased the voltage build up to the traction motors. It had been hoped that this would also reduce the incidence of flashovers, but while there was little improvement in the number of those there had been a reduction in their severity. These still occurred in the high speed section of the line and nearly always at over 80 mph (129 km/h) with the controller in the maximum notch.

One of the reasons for the flashovers on the main generator seems to have been oil contamination in the engine room; this was aggravated by the necessity to keep the bodyside windows shut to keep dirt and brake block dust out of the control gear. The oil mist in the engine room came from the engine air manifold drains and from oil leaks in the radiator fan gearbox. There were also oil leaks from the torque regulator (the Oily Octopus) connection block. By the use of better seals and with some alterations to the pipework the situation was considerably improved. As far as the traction motors were concerned, the trouble was associated with worn brushes and was improved by quicker renewal of these and by changing to a DE7 type brush; also during overhaul the motor armatures were vacuum-impregnated and wound with glass banding. The elimination of rail joints by the use of long welded rail also helped as did the removal of many points and crossings as a result of the upgrading of the main lines to the 100-mph (161-km/h) operation.

During 1972 the engine situation gradually improved and the piston problem was tackled by means of ultrasonic testing. Out of the 2,052 pistons installed 180 were found to be defective and of those 41 suffered from loose piston crowns. The cylinder blocks were being reclaimed by welding, reboring and honing and three engines were fitted with the latest pattern 42K liners. Modifications to

55019 'Royal Highland Fusilier' on the 08.05 from Kings Cross to Hull at Potters Bar in July 1979.

eliminate draughts from the drivers' cabs were carried out on No D9018 and, being apparently satisfactory, were then applied to the rest of the fleet.

In 1973 the engine situation was still improving with a failure rate of 65 in 52 weeks of operation; out of those 26 were due to liner seals, 10 to liner fracture and 11 to piston failures. The overall locomotive availability had gone up to 71 per cent from a low of 50 per cent in 1971 in time to take advantage of the next major speed-up resulting from the Civil Engineer's work on the East Coast route. That enabled journey times to be reduced to:-
Kings Cross to Leeds 185.8 miles (298 km) in 150 min 74.2 mph (119 km/h)
Kings Cross to Newcastle 268.3 miles (432 km) in 212 min 75.9 mph (122 km/h)
Kings Cross to Edinburgh 392.7 miles (632 km) in 330 min 71.2 mph (114 km/h)

In March Deltic No D9010 had paid a visit to Glasgow for an Open Day and in June a similar visit was paid by No D9004 to Inverness. The route indicator blinds were removed and vigilance control was in the process of being installed. Towards the end of 1973 the new re-numbering scheme was adopted, the first one being No D9019 which was allocated 55.019 on 22 November.

By 1974 the problem of liner leaks seemed to have been solved; but as soon as one problem is solved another comes along to take its place. Admittedly the engines were working harder with the faster schedules, but the failure rate was still at 73 in 52 weeks; of those 16 were due to fractured liners and 23 to pistons. There were slightly more failures of the quill shafts driving the water pumps which had continued throughout the life of these engines, but a new pattern was introduced with sulfanised anti-fretting treatment which it was hoped would improve matters. There were more cases of overheated radiators which caused loss of water and it was suspected that topping up with cold water might be having an adverse effect on the liners. 36 new radiators were supplied by the Marston Company and fitted while the others were flushed out at overhauls. A shortage of reconditioned engines put four locomotives back to next year's overhaul programme and the overall availability was 69 per cent compared with the target figure of 77 per cent. The mileage per casualty figure for 1974 was the best so far at 18,465 miles (29,715 km) against a target figure of 15,000 (24,140 km), so in spite of all their troubles the performance in service was as good as ever, better in fact.

By the middle of 1975 all of the 22 locomotives had passed the two-million mile (3,218,600-km) mark which represented an annual average of 154,000 miles (247,832 km); this was a slight deterioration over the figure achieved when the English Electric Company were

TABLE 1 D9007 Pinza

Date		Mileage (km)	Engine Changes
22. 6.61	To Doncaster		
30. 8.61	To Vulcan Foundry for bogie modifications		
2. 1.62	Exhaust drum defective		
26. 2.62	Annual	160,000 (257,488)	2
16. 4.62	No 4 traction motor		
13. 9.62	No 4 traction motor		
19. 9.62	No 1 engine; high water temperature 6 monthly		
22. 1.63	Annual examination	159,000 (255,879)	2
29. 5.63	Bogie defects		
12. 8.63	6 monthly		
23.10.63	No 2 engine; high water temperature		
31.10.63	Modifications		
7.12.63	No 2 engine; camshaft drive		
	Annual	127,000 (204,381)	2
23. 5.64	Cardan shaft splines worn		
12. 6.64	6 monthly		
30.10.64	Collision damage and annual	161,000 (259,097)	2
8. 2.65	Both engines short of water		
13. 8.65	High water temperatures		
19. 8.65	Radiators changed		
17. 9.65	No 1 engine; piston and connecting rod		1
27.11.65	Annual	163,000 (262,316)	2
21. 4 66	Fractured water pipe		
12. 1.67	Annual	94,000 (151,274)	2
10. 8.67	Water pump leak		
2.11.67	Overspeed trip	48,000 (77,246)	
8.12.67	Fractured oil pipe		
5. 4.68	Overhaul	70,000 (112,651)	2
27. 4 68	Fractured water pipe		
16.12.68	Overhaul	112,000 (180,242)	2
3. 2.69	Oil pipe fractured		
16. 2.69	Oil pipe fractured		
5. 8.69	No 1 engine changed		1
31. 8.69	Exhaust pipe lagging fire	102,000 (164,149)	2
31.12.69	No 2 engine changed		1

responsible for the maintenance, but E.E.Co. were under a penalty contract which certainly produced results. The tragedy of it was that they lost money on the contract and, allowing for the cost of the prototype and the costs involved in the class 23 'Baby Deltics', the whole batch of 33 locomotives must have cost them very dear.

There were renewed complaints about draughts in the cabs due to body flexing and some improvement was achieved when the air to the traction motor blowers in the nose ends was ducted in from below the cab floor. A further batch of new radiators was fitted to five of the fleet and four engines were fitted with the Mk IV pistons with the bolted on crown; those all ran well in excess of 6,000 hours and one even achieved 7,480 hours. Then it was decided to fit these as fast as possible, but supplies were delayed by a strike at Paxman's works. There were 73 engine failures in the year of which 13 were due to liners and 21 to pistons. All the heating boilers had been retubed with one scrapped leaving only one spare, and with the HST 125 sets planned to go into service in 1978 that was considered adequate. The boilers would only be needed for the night sleeper trains for which some new Mk III stock was planned for 1979.

A programme for the rewinding of the main generators was well under way and out of the 54 in service 28 had been rewound, four were at Derby Works and one at the GEC Traction (as the former English Electric was then known). For 1975 the miles per casualty were down to 12,590 (20,261 km) and the overall availability was 64 per cent.

With the advent of the Inter City 125 trains into service planned for 1978, the next two years were the last in which the Deltics were to provide the main motive power for the East Coast route. During those two years the performance was superb with higher than ever overall speeds, but availability was deteriorating. A typical report from York mentions that out of 41 trains booked to be worked by Deltics only 25 were actually run and the others had to be covered by class 47 power. At that time there were six Deltics in the works instead of the two normally planned, with a further three out of service for more than 12 hours in the day.

Deltic diagrams for 1977 were based on only 15 locomotives being available (68 per cent) and these diagrams for the period from Monday to Friday were as shown in Table 2. Engine failures were still running at 69 for the year of which only eight were due to liner fracture, but piston failures had gone up to 24 due to shortage of the Mk IV type. The record of individual locomotive mileage was kept up to the end of 1976 when the average was 2,339,060 miles (3,764,249 km) per locomotive; after that only a total fleet mileage was recorded. On the left is a life cycle of one typical locomotive, No D9007 'PINZA', from 1961 to 1977.

Date		Mileage (km)	Engine Changes
20. 3.70	Loss of cooling water		
24. 4.70	No 1 engine changed	122,000 (196,335)	1
23. 6.70	No 2 engine changed		1
15. 7.70	No 1 engine changed		1
12.10.70	No 1 engine changed; liner seal		1
4. 1.71	Overhaul	130,000 (209,209)	2
18.12.71	Overhaul	110,000 (177,023)	2
18. 8.72	No 2 engine changed		1
21. 9.72	Overhaul	180,000 (289,674)	2
18. 1.73	No 1 engine changed		1
30. 4.73	Water pump changed		
2. 7.73	No 2 engine changed		1
9. 8.73	Overhaul	65,000 (104,604)	2
16.10.73	No 2 engine changed; liner fracture		1
19.11.73	Fan drive gearbox defective		
30.11.73	Oil pipe leaking		
7.12.73	Main generator flashover		
1. 2.74	No 2 engine; connecting rod fracture		1

Total mileage: 1,803,000 (2,901,568 km)
Total casualties: 287
due to boiler: 69
due to Engines: 21
Renumbered 55.007

Date		Engine Changes
22. 8.74	Annual overhaul	2
5.12.74	No 1 engine changed	1
18. 1.75	No 2 engine changed	1
21. 2 75	No 1 engine changed	1
19. 8.75	Classified annual overhaul	2
5. 1.76	No 2 engine changed	1
25. 2.76	No 1 engine changed	1
1. 6.76	No 1 engine changed	1
6. 7.76	No 2 engine changed	1
19. 7.76	Both engines changed	2
8.11.76	Classified overhaul	2
18. 4.77	Both engines replaced	2

Mileage (estimated): 2,230,000 (3,588,739 km)
Engine changes: 55

55006 'The Fife & Forfar Yeomanry' near York with the up 14.20 train to Kings Cross in May 1980.

From June 1978 the HST began to take over the main Scottish services and on 1 May 1978 No 55022 carried the last Thistle Headboard to commemorate the end of locomotive haulage of the 'Flying Scotsman'. From then on it was to be an InterCity 125 service. Deltics were relegated to services to Hull, Cleethorpes and Scarborough. There were also a few foreign excursions with one in January from Paddington to Cardiff by No 55018 followed by an RPPR Special also on the Western Region by the same engine in February. On 5 March No 55003 took the 'Deltic Ranger' to Plymouth and that was followed by a run on the Southern Region when No 55007 hauled the 'Man of Kent' Special.

During 1978 modifications were still being carried out and in that year all the sandboxes were removed since they had been found to be almost useless; also by that year.all the engines had been fitted with the 42K liners and the Mk IV piston; a bit late in life, but they still had three years to go and were still using one set of pistons each year.

They were still working 15 diagrams, but not the same ones

TABLE 2
Deltic Diagrams: May 1977

			Arr	Dep
MON-FRI	No 1	Kings Cross		10.40
		Edinburgh	17.10	22.30
		Newcastle	00.49	00.59 in Depot 520 miles (837 km)
	No. 2	Newcastle		07.25
		Kings Cross	11.01	14.00
		Edinburgh	20.10	22.50
		Kings Cross	06.23	07.15 in Depot 1,060 miles (1,706 km)
	No 3	Kings Cross		09.00
		Newcastle	13.06	15.10
		Kings Cross	19.17	22.15
		Edinburgh	04.40	04.52 in Depot 1,060 miles (1,706 km)
	No 4	Edinburgh		08.00
		Kings Cross	13.38	16.00
		Edinburgh	21.43	00.05
		Kings Cross	06.55	08.15 in Depot 1,180 miles (1,899 km)
	No 5	Newcastle		05.05
		Edinburgh	09.19	12.00
		Kings Cross	17.53	20.00
		Newcastle	00.58	01.08 in Depot 790 miles (1,271 km)
	No 6	Newcastle		08.30
		Edinburgh	10.34	14.00
		Kings Cross	20.00	22.30
		Edinburgh	06.15	06.27 in Depot 930 miles (1,497 km)
	No 7	Edinburgh		09.50
		Kings Cross	15.18	18.04
		Leeds/ Bradford	22.25	23.00 in Depot 620 miles (998 km)
	No 8	Leeds		00.43
		Hull	04.53	06.50
		Kings Cross	09.55	11.25
		Leeds	13.58	17.30
		Kings Cross	20.06	23.55
		Newcastle	05.46	06.47 in Depot 850 miles (1,368 km)

55007 'Pinza' ends her days as York Station pilot, shunting empty stock over the River Ouse.

		Arr	Dep	
No 9	Kings Cross		08.00	
	Edinburgh	14.13	16.00	
	Kings Cross	21.56	22.45	in Depot 800 miles (1,287 km)
No 10	Kings Cross		01.15	
	Leeds	05.05	07.30	
	Kings Cross	10.00	12.25	
	Edinburgh	18.07	20.20	
	Kings Cross	05.10	06.35	in Depot 1,110 miles (1,786 km)
No 11	Leeds		06.00	
	Bradford	06.34	07.20	
	Kings Cross	10.08	18.00	
	Newcastle	21.39	22.20	in Depot 450 miles (724 km)
No 12	Newcastle		09.20	
	Kings Cross	13.07	17.00	
	Edinburgh	22.40	22.52	in Depot 670 miles (1,078 km)
No 13	Edinburgh		00.40	
	Kings Cross	07.14	10.00	
	Edinburgh	15.27	17.00	
	Kings Cross	22.57	23.45	in Depot 1,190 miles (1,915 km)
No 14	Kings Cross		07.45	
	Edinburgh	13.20	15.00	
	Kings Cross	20.37	22.45	
	Newcastle	03.10	03.20	in Depot 1,060 miles (1,706 km)
No 15	Newcastle		08.30	
	Kings Cross	12.25	15.55	
	Leeds	18.25	20.08	
	Harrogate	20.35	20.56	
	Leeds	22.03	23.42	in Depot 530 miles (853 km)

Circuit Sequence		
	1-2-3-4-1	4,340 miles (6,984 km)
	5	3,950 miles (6,357 km)
	6-7-8-6	3,950 miles (6,356 km)
	11-12-13-14-15-11	3,900 miles (6,276 km)
	9-10-9	4,620 miles (7,435 km)

as in 1977, and were putting up some good runs such as that of No 55016 which on 10 April ran the 188 miles (302 km) from York to Kings Cross in 133 minutes (84.8 mph/136 km/h). The improvement in operating speeds over the life of these Deltics is shown by the comparative schedules from 1962 to 1978 in Table 3. A comparable HST timing is also shown by way of comparison.

During 1978 in spite of the engines all being fitted with the latest modifications there were still 53 failures in the year, 11 of which were due to liners and 10 to pistons. In seven of the piston failures the connecting rods came through the crankcases and most of those failures were attributed to the gudgeon pin housing.

Since both the HST delivery programme and the supply of Mk III sleepers with ETH were running late, there was anxiety as to whether the boilers would last out to the planned withdrawal dates which were six locomotives each in 1981/2/3 and the final four in 1984.

Some of the Deltics had been transferred to the NE/SW routes from Newcastle to Bristol via Sheffield, Derby and Birmingham

55016 'Gordon Highlander' approaching a 20-mph (32-km/h) speed restriction for East Coast refurbishing in 1980.

and on the Trans-Pennine route from Leeds to Liverpool and there were plans to transfer the whole fleet to those services, but the cost of maintenance and the problems of retraining staff and stocking new depots overruled that scheme. From 1979 the Deltics made many more visits to other Regions and during 1980, their last year of operation, the following specials were worked:-
25 May 'Deltic Fenman II'
Locomotive No 55009
12 September 'Deltic Anglian'
Locomotive No 55007
17 October 'Wessex Deltic'
Locomotive No 55015
28 November 'Deltic Devonian'
Locomotive No 55016
28 November 'York-Paddington'
Locomotive No 55022

By June 1981 Nos 55001/3/5/6 and 55020 had been withdrawn and the last service run was to York behind No 55021 on 31 December 1981. A farewell 'Deltic Tribute' run was held on 2 Jan 1982.

In addition to the Prototype Deltic in the Science Museum no less than four have been preserved, the highest percentage of any locomotives ever built. These four are:-
55002 (9002) at the National Railway Museum at York,
55009 (9009) and 55019 (9019) at the North Yorkshire Moors Railway,
55022 (9000) at the Nene Valley Railway.

TABLE 3

	miles (km)	class 1962	minutes class 55 1968	class 55 1978	HST 1980
Kings Cross					
Potters Bar	12.7 (20)	15	13½	13	11½
Hatfield	17.7 (28)	19	17½	17	
Hitchin	31.9 (51)	31	27½	26½	22
Sandy	41.4 (66)	39	35	34	28
Huntingdon	58.9 (95)	52	44½	43	35½
Peterborough	76.3 (123)	67	60½	54	44
Essendine	88.6 (142)	78	71	61½	
Stoke Box	100.1 (161)	87	78½	69	56½
Grantham	105.5 (170)	91	87½	72½	60
Newark	120.1 (193)	105	92	81	68
Retford	138.6 (223)	124	106	92	78
Doncaster	156 (251)	140	124	106	96
Overall average speed mph (km)		66.8 (107.5)	75.4 (121.3)	88.3 (142.1)	97.5 (156.9)

There is also a possibility that 55015 'Tulyar' may be saved and negotiations are continuing.

The last officially recorded mileage for the whole Deltic fleet was 63,178,916 miles (101,673,830 km) as at October 1980 and allowing a reasonable figure for 1981 the total would have amounted to 65,130,000 (104,813,710 km) or 2.96 million miles (4,763,528 km) per locomotive. As the Scottish-based locomotives put in a consistently higher mileage than the others, there is a good chance that some of them actually exceeded the three million mile (4,827,900 km) mark, but unfortunately that cannot be officially claimed.

These Deltic locomotives could be entitled the 'Concorde' of the railway world and we shall never see their like again. It might be argued that their job could have been done more economically by using two class 37s, but that would have entailed carting round an extra 100 tons (101,606 kg) with every train. Certainly their cost per mile would have been much less and the makers would have made a profit out of them, but the Deltics enabled the East Coast route to offer a service that could only have been achieved by electrification and there was a very slim chance of that. In British eyes a heroic failure is more highly prized than mere success by itself and the Deltics certainly come into that category.

Enigma and Variations

Apart from the two main classes of Deltic diesel-electric locomotives (classes 23 and 55) mention must be made of a special prototype locomotive that was 'almost a Deltic'. The locomotive was numbered DP2 and was just like a Deltic in appearance with the same bogies, cabs and nose ends, but the bodywork between the cabs was adapted to contain the English Electric 16-cylinder 10-in (25-cm) bore VEE engine which had then just been uprated to 2,700 hp. That engine which had first been used in the LMS locomotive No 10000 at a rating of 1,600 hp in 1947 had been strengthened internally to cope with the higher output and was then known as the 16CSVT (C=Charge cooled; S=Supercharged; V=VEE formation and T=Traction version). This was part of an exercise to satisfy the British Transport Commission's need for a locomotive of at least 2,500 hp on a Co-Co wheel arrangement and met that specification exactly.

It had been found necessary to convince the BTC that the uprated engine would give a satisfactory performance and the best way of doing that was to put it on a rail vehicle and run it. What with the delays due to the late deliveries of the Deltics and the class 37s it did not get the priority it should have had and was put back to the tail end of the Deltic programme; thus it did not come into service until May 1962 by which time it was too late to affect the BTC which was in favour of the Sulzer 2,750-hp engine for that duty.

DP2 was the third prototype locomotive in this category, which became known as the Type 4½, the other two being the Brush 'Falcon' which had two Maybach high speed diesel engines producing 2,800 hp and the 'Lion' which was built by a consortium consisting of Sulzer Bros, the Associated Electrical Industries

DP2 passing the rival Works at Rugby in 1962.

and the Birmingham Railway Carriage & Wagon Company. DP2 was some 10 tons (10,160 kg) lighter than the other two and weighed 104 tons (105,670 kg) of which the engine weight was 19.4 tons (19,712 kg). Its cost was considerably less than that of a Deltic and worked out at just over £100,000 exclusive of the development costs of the uprated engine.

After a year of operation in the London Midland Region it was transferred to the Eastern Region in the summer of 1963 when it was put onto a regular Deltic diagram so that one Deltic could be taken out of service for the boilers to be prepared for the winter season. During its 58 days of Deltic standby duty it ran 43,000 miles (69,200 km) which was even more than the Deltics were doing at that time, but for the rest of its time it was sadly under-used since there were virtually no other runs in the timetable at that time where its full power could be employed; it was put onto such runs as the Sheffield Pullman where its full output was only used for about 25 per cent of the journey. It was leased to British Rail at 2/6d (12½p) per mile and after running 627,000 miles (1,009,031 km) in five years was tragically wrecked in an accident at Thirsk in July 1967. On that day DP2 was filling in for a Deltic and was running at 100 mph (161 km/h) on a Scotch express when it was flagged down for a freight train that had become derailed on the adjacent slow line. It could not stop in time and the locomotive was ripped all along one side and, though the driver was luckily unharmed five of the passengers were killed and DP2 was wrecked.

With the insurance and the rental return English Electric probably did quite well out of that locomotive which put on a superb performance and was always reckoned by the Eastern Region as the best locomotive they ever had, particularly in its last year when it was fitted with electronic load control. The merits of that function were shown up best on the difficult section of line between Newcastle and Edinburgh where there were some twelve speed restrictions in the 124.5 miles (201 km) and DP2 could keep the Deltic timings of 114 minutes with a 450-ton

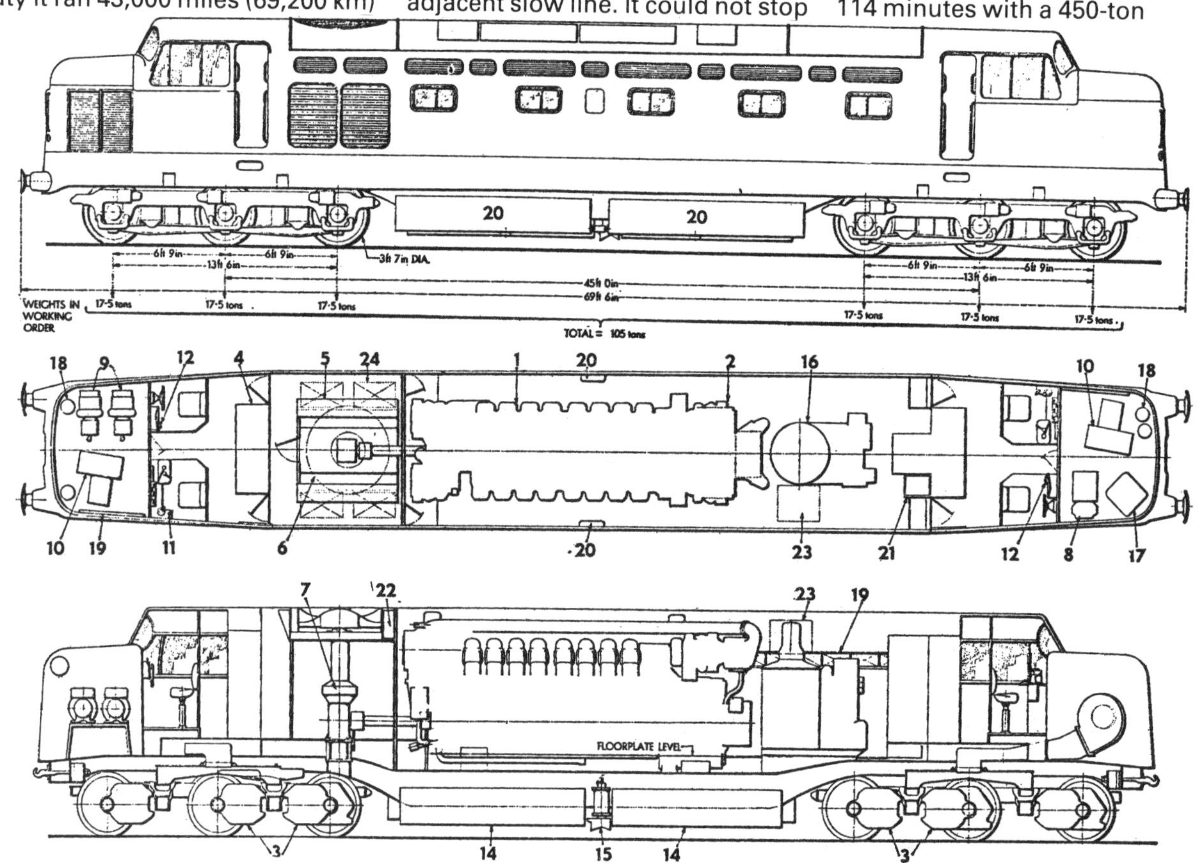

Layout of EE 2,700 bhp prototype diesel-electric Co-Co locomotive no. DP2

1 EE 16 CSVT 2,700 bhp diesel engine
2 Main generator
3 Traction motor
4 No. 1 equipment frame
5 Radiator panels
6 Radiator fan
7 Magnetic coupling
8 Air compressor
9 Vacuum exhausters
10 Traction motor blower
11 Driver's brake valves
12 Hotplate
14 Water tank
15 Water scoop
16 Train heating boiler
17 WC
18 Fire extinguisher CO_2 bottle
19 Panel-type air filter
20 (Side elevation) Fuel tank
20 (Plan) Water filling ducts
21 Cooker and No 2 equipment frame
22 Header tank
23 Emergency fuel tank
24 Battery

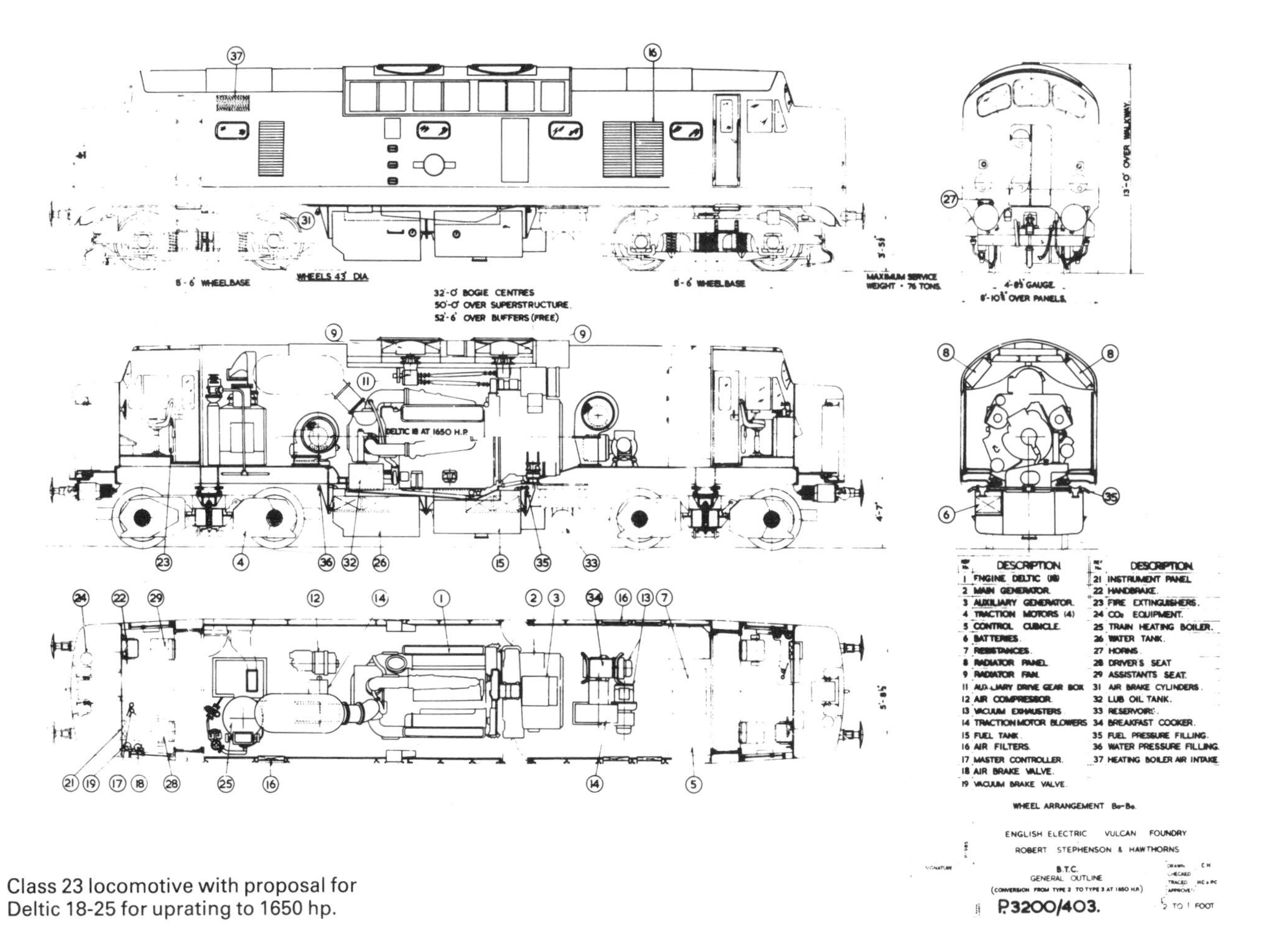

Class 23 locomotive with proposal for Deltic 18-25 for uprating to 1650 hp.

DP2 at the Vulcan Works after its accident in July 1967 at Thirsk.

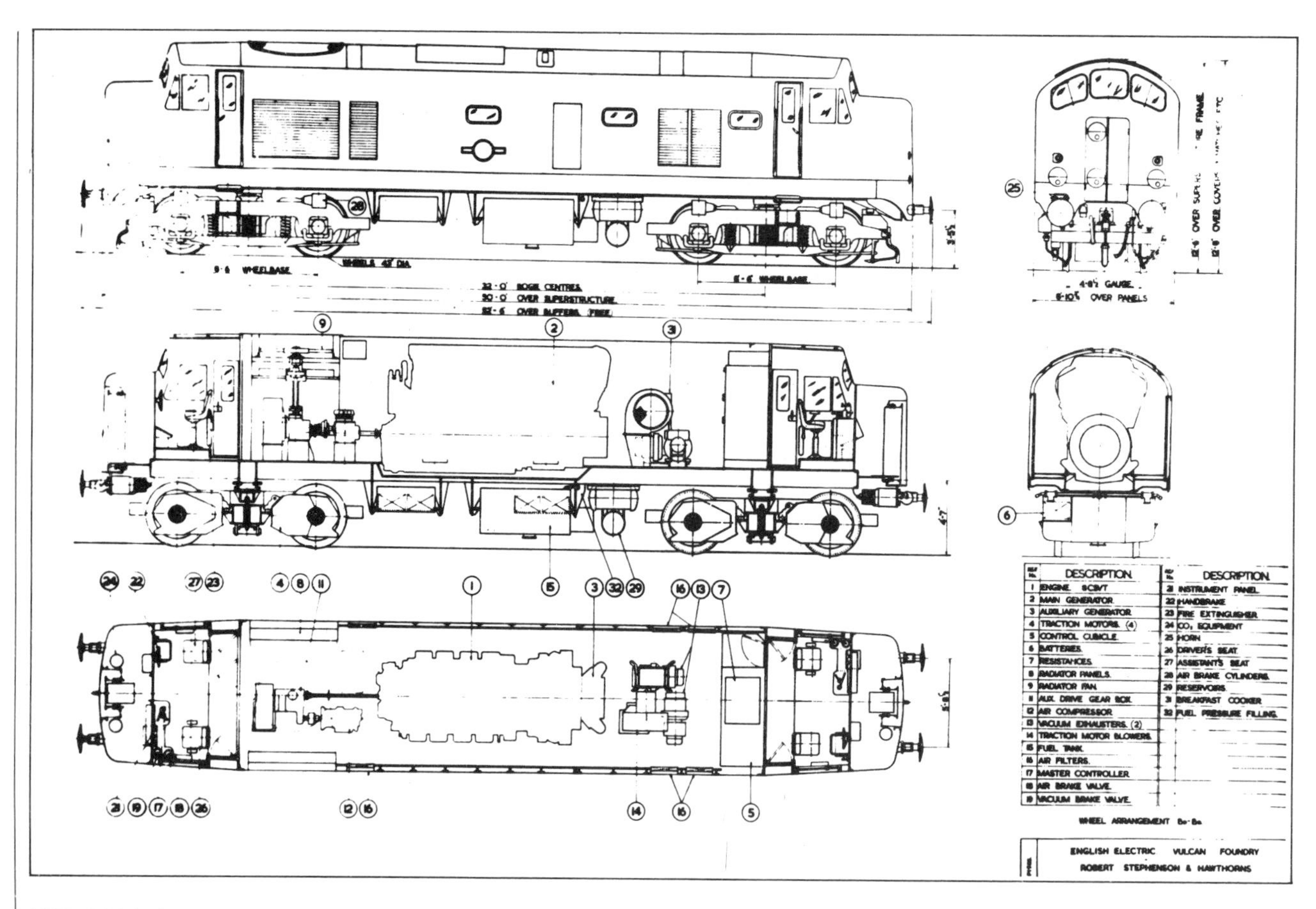

Class 23 locomotive with proposed English Electric 8 CSVT diesel engine at 1250 hp.

(457,229 kg) train. That time was the same as the record run of the North Eastern 4-4-0 No 1620 in the Race to the North of 1895 for that section of the journey. A log of DP2's run over that section is given in Table 4.

As a result of the excellent performance put up by DP2 English Electric got an order for 50 similar locomotives that became the class 50 and are now on the Western Region.

Some of the equipment including the power unit was salvaged from the wreck of DP2 and that became a spare engine for the class 50. By way of contrast that was the only spare engine for 50 of those locomotives whereas the 22 Deltics required 13 engines to keep them in service.

There are some other interesting aspects of the Deltic story and one of these concerns the Prototype Deltic (DP1). During its time on the LM Region in 1957 it had hauled a special train containing a Canadian Trade Mission and there had been a scheme to send the Deltic to Canada on a sales tour. In order to meet the Canadian requirements and to make it suitable for operation in Canada a number of modifications would have been necessary which included:-

1. Fitting of Canadian airbrake system with a compressor having a capacity of at least 200 cu ft per min
2. Automatic couplers and AAR draftgear
3. New American standard 42 in (107 cm) monobloc wheels
4. Extra train heating capacity

TABLE 4
Co-Co Diesel No DP2 12 coaches 455 tons

	Distance miles (km)	Scheduled minutes	Actual	Maximum speed mph (km/h)
Newcastle				
Morpeth	16.6 (26.7)	17½	19.42	82 (132)
Alnmouth	34.8 (56)	32½	34.56	81 (130)
Belford	51.6 (83)	46	48.49	88 (142)
Tweedmouth	65.8 (106)	60	59.55	88 (142)
Granthouse	83.3 (134)	77	76.53	73 (117)
Dunbar	95.3 (153)	87	86.54	82 (132)
Drem	106.7 (172)	97	96.18	81 (130)
Monktonhall	118.1 (190)	106	105.37	78 (125)
Edinburgh	124.5 (200)	114	114.55	46 (74)

5. Relocation of driver's position in cab
6. Canadian headlamps and marker code
7. Extra radiator capacity for higher ambient conditions
8. Extra cab heaters and demisters for Canadian winter
9. Cowcatchers
10. Structure suitable for 400 ton (406,426 kg) buffing load
11. Radio telephone

When the cost of all that was worked out the scheme was dropped. It is very doubtful if it could have stood up to Canadian operating conditions anyway.

There were a considerable number of schemes proposed for the class 23 'Baby Deltics' at one time or another around their rest period of 1962. Apart from the possible fitting of the 12UT engine rated at 1,550 hp for which No D5901 went to the Vulcan Foundry works there were schemes to re-equip the rest with 18-cylinder Deltic engines in order to convert them into a Type 3 or to fit the English Electric 8CSVT engine then rated at 1,250 hp; though the latter would have made a good, reliable locomotive it would have been both underpowered and overweight with an axle load of at least 20 tons (20,321 kg). British Rail did even ask English Electric if they could possibly find another customer for those ten locomotives, but it would have taken a supreme effort of salesmanship in view of their reputation by that time. Between 1958 and 1966 there were a number of locomotive designs submitted for consideration in which Deltic engines were offered and those included:-

A Bo-Bo design with a Deltic 18-27 engine at 2,500 hp with steam heating at a weight of 78 tons (79,253 kg)

A Bo-Bo design as above without steamheating, but with electric heating at 72 tons (73,157 kg)

A Co-Co with two Deltic nine-cylinder engines at 2,500 hp with steam heating at 99 tons (100,590 kg)

A B-B with two Deltic nine-cylinder engines and hydraulic transmission with steam heating at 74 tons (75,189 kg)

A Co-Co with two Deltic 18-27 engines giving 4,400 hp with electric heating at a weight of 114 tons (115,831 kg)

The latter were known as the 'Super Deltics', but like the Brush 'Kestrel' built in 1967 with an output of 4,000 hp they would have been too heavy to have been allowed to work at 125 mph (201 km/h) which was the basic reason for the higher power requirement.

Among the other Deltic designs there was an ugly Guppy-like object only 37 ft 6 in (11.5 m) long with the 18-cylinder engine on a Bo-Bo wheelbase weighing 64 tons (65,028 kg) proposed for Australia, but perhaps fortunately that was never delivered. It was an unfortunate effect that the submission of Deltic type locomotives as the premier offer killed English Electric's chance of getting the order with their conventional engine since customers got the impression that the makers thought of it as second rate and a lot of business was lost through that.

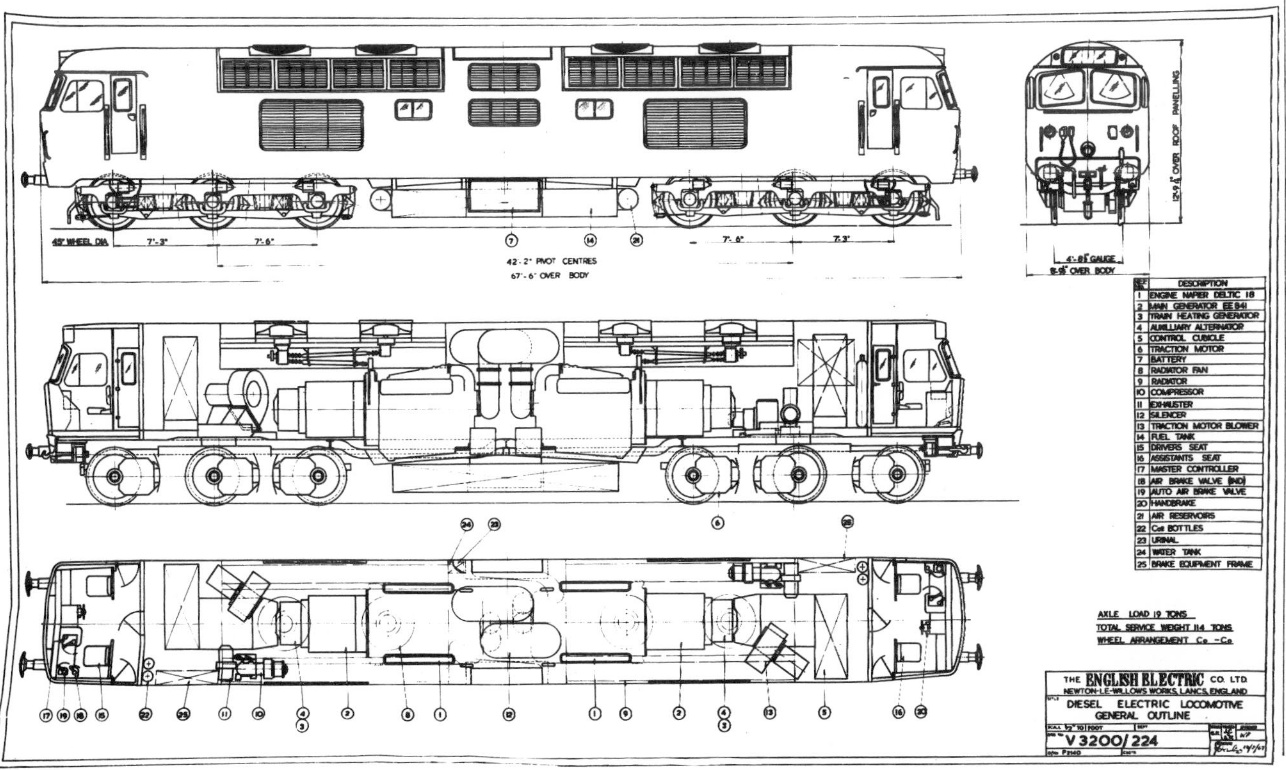

The Super Deltic of 4400 hp, proposed in 1967.

Deltic Locomotives Class 55

Original Number	Date Delivered	Name	Final Number
D.9000	28.2.61	Royal Scots Grey	55.022
D.9001	23.2.61	St. Paddy	55.001
D.9002	9.3.61	The King's Own Yorkshire Light Infantry	55.002
D.9003	27.3.61	Meld	55.003
D.9004	18.5.61	Queen's Own Highlander	55.004
D.9005	25.5.61	The Prince of Wales's Own Regiment of Yorkshire	55.005
D.9006	29.6.61	The Fife & Forfar Yeomanry	55.006
D.9007	22.6.61	Pinza	55.007
D.9008	7.7.61	The Green Howards	55.008
D.9009	21.7.61	Alycidon	55.009
D.9010	24.7.61	The King's Own Scottish Borderer	55.010
D.9011	24.8.61	The Royal Northumberland Fusiliers	55.011
D.9012	4.9.61	Crepello	55.012
D.9013	14.9.61	The Black Watch	55.013
D.9014	29.9.61	The Duke of Wellington's Regiment	55.014
D.9015	13.10.61	Tulyar	55.015
D.9016	27.10.61	Gordon Highlander	55.016
D.9017	5.11.61	The Durham Light Infantry	55.017
D.9018	24.11.61	Ballymos	55.018
D.9019	29.12.61	Royal Highland Fusilier	55.019
D.9020	12.2.62	Nimbus	55.020
D.9021	2.5.62	Argyll & Sutherland Highlander	55.021

The publishers wish to thank the following for their help with the illustrations:

Colour Rail: pp. 17, 18, 19, 21 (inset), 22 (top), 23 (top), 24 (bottom).
GEC Traction: pp. 1, 6-7, 10, 15 (top), 23 (btm), 25, 26, 27, 30, 31 (top), 35 (btm), 40, 52, 56.
Alan Oliver: 20 (btm), 22 (btm), 24 (top).
Paxman Diesels: pp. 4, 5, 8, 9.
W.A. Sharman: pp. 20-21.
R.H.G. Simpson: p. 37
Brian Webb: pp. 32, 35 (top), 38 (top), 42, 44, 45, 48.

D.9013 on down train of Mk I stock in 1966, arriving at York.